Volumes in this series

THE ADVENTURES OF HUCKLEBERRY FINN by Mark Twain.
THE ADVENTURES OF TOM SAWYER by Mark Twain.
Artist: C. WALTER HODGES
BLACK BEAUTY by Anna Sewell. *Artist:* LUCY KEMP-WELCH
THE BROWNIES AND OTHER STORIES by Mrs Ewing.
Artist: E. H. SHEPARD
THE CORAL ISLAND by R. M. Ballantyne. *Artist:* LEO BATES
THE CUCKOO CLOCK by Mary Louisa Molesworth. *Artist:* E. H. SHEPARD
FAIRY TALES FROM THE ARABIAN NIGHTS. Edited by E. Dixon.
Artist: JOAN KIDDELL-MONROE
FAIRY TALES OF LONG AGO. Edited by M. C. Carey.
Artist: D. J. WATKINS-PITCHFORD
GRIMMS' FAIRY TALES. *Artist:* CHARLES FOLKARD
GULLIVER'S TRAVELS by Jonathan Swift. *Artist:* ARTHUR RACKHAM
HANS ANDERSEN'S FAIRY TALES. *Artist:* MAXWELL ARMFIELD
HEIDI by Johanna Spyri. *Artist:* VINCENT O. COHEN
LITTLE WOMEN by Louisa M. Alcott. *Artist:* S. VAN ABBÉ
GOOD WIVES by Louisa M. Alcott. *Artist:* S. VAN ABBÉ
PILGRIM'S PROGRESS by John Bunyan. *Artist:* FRANK C. PAPÉ
PINOCCHIO: THE STORY OF A PUPPET by Carlo Collodi.
Artist: CHARLES FOLKARD
THE PRINCESS AND THE GOBLIN by George MacDonald.
THE PRINCESS AND CURDIE by George MacDonald.
Artist: CHARLES FOLKARD
ROBIN HOOD by Carola Oman. *Artist:* S. VAN ABBÉ
ROBINSON CRUSOE by Daniel Defoe. *Artist:* J. AYTON-SYMINGTON
SWISS FAMILY ROBINSON by J. R. Wyss. *Artist:* CHARLES FOLKARD
TOM BROWN'S SCHOOLDAYS by Thomas Hughes. *Artist:* S. VAN ABBÉ
TREASURE ISLAND by R. L. Stevenson. *Artist:* S. VAN ABBÉ
A WONDER BOOK by Nathaniel Hawthorne. *Artist:* S. VAN ABBÉ
TANGLEWOOD TALES by Nathaniel Hawthorne. *Artist:* S. VAN ABBÉ
THE WONDERFUL ADVENTURES OF NILS by Selma Lagerlöf.
THE FURTHER ADVENTURES OF NILS by Selma Lagerlöf.
Artist: HANS BAUMHAUER
HANS BRINKER by Mary Mapes Dodge. *Artist:* HANS BAUMHAUER

Larger size (Demy 8vo)

ALICE'S ADVENTURES IN WONDERLAND AND
THROUGH THE LOOKING-GLASS by Lewis Carroll.
Artist: JOHN TENNIEL
THE CHILDREN OF THE NEW FOREST by Captain Marryat.
Artist: LIONEL EDWARDS
DON QUIXOTE by Cervantes. *Artist:* W. HEATH ROBINSON
KING ARTHUR AND THE ROUND TABLE by A. M. Hadfield.
Artist: DONALD SETON CAMMELL
LORNA DOONE by R. D. Blackmore. *Artist:* LIONEL EDWARDS
MODERN FAIRY STORIES. Edited by R. L. Green. *Artist:* E. H. SHEPARD
AT THE BACK OF THE NORTH WIND by George MacDonald.
Artist: E. H. SHEPARD

THE BOOK OF
NONSENSE

by many authors

CHOSEN AND ARRANGED BY
ROGER LANCELYN GREEN, *ed.*

With four colour plates by
CHARLES FOLKARD

*and many contemporary illustrations
in the text*

NEW YORK: E. P. DUTTON & CO. INC

Copyright, ©, 1956
by
E. P. DUTTON & CO. INC.
Printed in U.S.A.

Colored Illustrations Printed in Great Britain

Library of Congress Catalog Card Number: 56—12852

CONTENTS

v

CONTENTS   ix

ILLUSTRATIONS

COLOUR PLATES

by Charles Folkard

BLACK AND WHITE DRAWINGS

INTRODUCTION

(With Nonsense in it)

MANY learned and sensible people have tried to decide what Nonsense is—or at least they have tried to discover the difference between Nonsense and Tommy Rot: between the sort of thing Lewis Carroll and Edward Lear wrote, and the sort of thing we all sometimes write without even trying. But no one has really discovered the secret: they can tell us what they think it is that makes 'The Walrus and the Carpenter' or 'The Owl and the Pussy Cat' so good and so pleasing, but they cannot tell us how to plant a Bong-tree of our own, or picnic again on the beach which was so sandy that seven maids with seven mops could not clear it in six months.

We can all agree, however, that Lewis Carroll wrote the best Nonsense of any one—and we all know *Alice's Adventures in Wonderland* and *Through the Looking-Glass* so well that we would never need to read them again—if they did not prove themselves two of the best books ever written by being just as fresh and amusing whenever we decide that we really cannot resist dipping into them just once more.

Both the Alice stories form together a companion volume to this one, so only a few of the Nonsense poems contained in them will be found here—the ones which are so much the best of their kind ever written that they could not possibly be left out: 'Jabberwocky,' 'The Walrus and the Carpenter,' and 'The Aged, Aged Man.' There are also two sets of verses rather like two in *Wonderland*; but neither of them is quite the same, and so make interesting poems on their own.

Now it may seem that Nonsense is very easy to write: but it appears to be much more difficult than Sense. Yet perhaps Lewis Carroll did so well because he was such a sensible man, and spent so much of his time over Mathematics and Logic—in neither of which is there any Nonsense at all.

Yet he was perfectly logical when he made the White Knight say:

> 'But I was thinking of a plan
>   To dye one's whiskers green,
> And always use so large a fan
>   That they could not be seen.'

Only the logic is Looking-Glass Logic, and the result is one of the most perfectly *right* scraps of Nonsense ever written. We can see, to some extent, how he did this—which does not mean that we could do it ourselves. But what about the chorus at the Looking-Glass Banquet?

> Then fill up the glasses with treacle and ink,
> Or anything else that is pleasant to drink;
> Mix sand with the cider, and wool with the wine—
> And welcome Queen Alice with ninety-times-nine!

That, surely, is just an unlikely, contradictory sort of muddle which anybody could write! But not a bit of it: a very clever dramatist, Henry Saville Clarke, who made the Alice books into a play in 1886, wanted another stanza (and he could write fairly good songs of the ordinary or Sensible kind): but this was the best he could do in the way of Nonsense:

> Sound the festal trumpets, set the bells a-ringing,
> Here are curried crumpets, crocodiles and beans:
> Raise on high the chalice, in our honour singing,
> Welcome, welcome Alice, with the noble Queens.

Curried crumpets certainly go well with crocodiles, but nevertheless Lewis Carroll *could* write Nonsense, and Saville Clarke just could not:

> For though he wrote it all by rote,
> He did not write it right!

If you do not believe me, try an even easier kind of Nonsense. In *Wonderland* Lewis Carroll usually parodied famous poems fairly closely: 'Twinkle, twinkle little star' became:

> Twinkle, twinkle, little bat!
> How I wonder what you 're at!
> Up above the world you fly,
> Like a tea-tray in the sky.

It would be an amusing kind of competition to try and follow this with a parody of the next stanza. Something like this, perhaps:

> Then the oyster and the shark
> Thank you for your kindly bark;
> They could not see which way to row
> If you did not tinkle so.

'I know what that *doesn't* make,' as Bruno said in his spelling lesson—and that is anything like real Nonsense: and it 's not for want of trying—or of reading as much Nonsense as I could possibly find!

For of course Lewis Carroll did not write all the Nonsense

—nor did Edward Lear write all the rest of it: and neither of them invented it.

Lear did not even invent the 'Limerick' in which so many of his best Nonsense Rhymes were written. When he started inventing his (in about 1832, though they were not published until 1846), he modelled them on the rhymes in a booklet called *Anecdotes and Adventures of Fifteen Gentlemen* published about 1822, whose author is unknown—and in particular on this one:

> There was a sick man of Tobago
> Lived long on rice-gruel and sago;
> But at last, to his bliss,
> The physician said this:
> 'To a roast leg of mutton you may go.'

Even then the *kind* of verse was not really new, for there were such well-known Nursery Rhymes as:

> Hickory, Dickory, Dock!
> The Mouse ran up the Clock:
> The Clock struck 'One!'
> The Mouse was gone!
> Hickory, Dickory, Dock!

This, and the similar rhyme about the Pig that flew up in the air, are often thought to be about Richard Cromwell— and so must have been written about 1660, when General Monk, 'The Man in Brown,' brought him down very quickly from the throne when he had only been Lord Protector for one year. And even if the Mouse was not Oliver's son, the rhyme was already in print by 1744.

Many of the Nursery Rhymes are really Nonsense Rhymes, and most of them are very old: often we can only find the dates when they were first written down (these are the dates after the rhymes in this book)—but some we know for certain were well known hundreds of years earlier, even if not quite in the same words. Look, for example, at the poem called 'Namby-Pamby,' and you will see how many of them Henry Carey knew in 1725—and probably heard years earlier when he was a child.

We do not know who made up nearly all of the Nursery Rhymes; and there are still rhymes being repeated of which we know neither the age nor the author. Who, for example, invented what is perhaps the most famous limerick of all, 'The young lady of Riga,' and when did he do it? I don't think that the answer is known. But it was already a very familiar rhyme in 1888 when Andrew Lang wrote about:

> . . . her of whom old stories tell:
> She loved a Tiger passing well
> (A nymph was she of stately Riga)
> And once came back—inside the Tiger.

Nor does anyone seem to know when or by whom the verses were invented about those two famous dead men who got up to fight—and there are several others which you will find near the end of this book, with an odd collection of short rhymes of various sorts. Some of these are, most unexpectedly, by famous authors: and some only look like nonsense, but are perfectly sensible if you read them in the right way.

Nonsense seems to be as old as literature (but most of it has got lost on the way). Even the ancient Greeks had a pretty good idea of it, as when Lucilius wrote about Marcus who ran all night and was still at the starting-place in the morning—just as Alice and the Red Queen were after their Looking-Glass race.

In this *Book of Nonsense* I have tried to show that other

people besides Lear and Lewis Carroll *did* write it, both before and since, and some of them very well indeed. But probably *Through the Looking-Glass* remains, and may always remain, the greatest Nonsense book ever written—both in prose and verse. Lewis Carroll wrote other things, which are included here: some of his letters to children might be paragraphs from *Alice*, and no one has even written a long Nonsense poem which can compare with *The Hunting of the Snark*. Even Lear was usually better with shorter verses, though 'The Owl and the Pussy Cat' and 'The Pobble who has no Toes' are perfect throughout: but often he had really said all that he had to say in one stanza, and then repeated himself, with variations—as in the sad case of 'Uncle Arly':

> O my aged Uncle Arly!
> Sitting on a heap of Barley
>   Through the silent hours of night—
> Close beside a leafy thicket—
> On his nose there was a Cricket—
> In his hat a Railway Ticket—
>   (But his shoes were far too tight).

This is a splendid beginning, but the other six stanzas add nothing to it. And, in a different way, 'The Dong with the Luminous Nose,' that strange, weird poem, just fails to be Nonsense at all, in spite of a stray reference to 'Oblong Oysters' and the description of how he made 'a Nose as strange as a Nose could be.'

Which brings us back to where we started, with the question 'What is Nonsense?'

Perhaps the nearest we can get is the nearest that Lewis Carroll himself could when he said of the *Alice* books that 'every idea and nearly every word of the dialogue, *came of*

itself. . . . Whenever or however it comes, *it comes of itself.*
I cannot set invention going like a clock, by any voluntary
winding up.' And *The Hunting of the Snark* came to him
in just this way also: 'I was walking on a hillside, alone, one
bright summer day, when suddenly there came into my
head one line of verse—one solitary line—"For the Snark
was a Boojum, you see." I knew not what it meant, then:
I know not what it means, now; but I wrote it down: and,
some time afterwards, the rest of the stanza occurred to me,
that being its last line: and so, by degrees, at odd moments
during the next year or two, the rest of the poem pieced
itself together, that being its last stanza.' *And that was The —ll*

'And the moral of that is,' surely, that, like the Caucus-
race, 'the best way to explain it is to do it.' But only a few
people can do it—and, as it takes someone like Lewis
Carroll to begin at the end and make such a successful
middle on his way to the beginning, the best thing to do
now is to turn over the page, and as the King of Hearts
suggested 'begin at the beginning, and go on till you come
to the end: then stop.'

R. L. G.

ACKNOWLEDGMENTS

FOR permission to quote copyright material, the editor's and publishers' ack-
nowledgments and thanks are due to John Murray Ltd for 'There was an Old
Person of Diss' from *Teapots and Quails* by Edward Lear; to the executors of
E. Nesbit for two verses by E. Nesbit; to the executors of Andrew Lang for
The Garden of Regrets; to Professor C. S. Lewis and the *Atlantic Monthly* for
Awake, My Lute!; to Mr H. D. Molesworth for *A Race* by Mrs Molesworth; to
the executors of Sir Edward Parry for *The Fisherman on Toast* from *Gamble
Gold*; to the executors of Hilaire Belloc for *Hildebrand* from *Cautionary Tales
for Children*; to Methuen and Co. Ltd and E. P. Dutton and Co. Inc. for *Lines
and Squares* from *When We Were Very Young* (copyright), 1952, by A. A.
Milne, and *Hums of Pooh* from *Winnie the Pooh* (copyright), 1954, by A. A.
Milne, both with illustrations by E. H. Shepard; to the Estate of Lewis Carroll
for ten letters from *Letters to Child-Friends*; to Macmillan and Co. Ltd for
illustrations by Henry Holiday, Sir John Tenniel, and Harry Furniss.

'Twas brillig, and the slithy toves
  Did gyre and gimble in the wabe;
All mimsy were the borogoves,
  And the mome raths outgrabe.

LEWIS CARROLL. (*1855.*)

PROLOGUE

JABBERWOCKY

'Twas brillig, and the slithy toves
   Did gyre and gimble in the wabe;
All mimsy were the borogoves,
   And the mome raths outgrabe.

'Beware the Jabberwock, my son!
   The jaws that bite, the claws that catch!
Beware the Jubjub bird, and shun
   The frumious Bandersnatch!'

He took his vorpal sword in hand:
   Long time the manxome foe he sought—
So rested he by the Tumtum tree,
   And stood awhile in thought.

And while in uffish thought he stood,
   The Jabberwock, with eyes of flame,
Came whiffling through the tulgey wood,
   And burbled as it came!

One, two! One, two! And through and through
   The vorpal blade went snicker-snack!
He left it dead, and with its head
   He went galumphing back.

1

'And hast thou slain the Jabberwock?
  Come to my arms, my beamish boy!
O frabjous day!   Callooh!   Callay!'
  He chortled in his joy.

'Twas brillig, and the slithy toves
  Did gyre and gimble in the wabe:
All mimsy were the borogoves,
  And the mome raths outgrabe.

Lewis Carroll (1855 and 1871).

THE HUNTING OF THE SNARK

By LEWIS CARROLL

FIT THE FIRST

The Landing

'Just the place for a Snark!' the Bellman cried,
  As he landed his crew with care;
Supporting each man on the top of the tide
  By a finger entwined in his hair.

'Just the place for a Snark!   I have said it twice:
  That alone should encourage the crew.
Just the place for a Snark!   I have said it thrice:
  What I tell you three times is true.'

The crew was complete: it included a Boots—
  A maker of Bonnets and Hoods—
A Barrister, brought to arrange their disputes—
  And a Broker, to value their goods.

A Billiard-marker, whose skill was immense,
  Might perhaps have won more than his share—
But a Banker, engaged at enormous expense,
  Had the whole of their cash in his care.

3

There was also a Beaver, that paced on the deck,
   Or would sit making lace in the bow:
And had often (the Bellman said) saved them from
      wreck,
   Though none of the sailors knew how.

There was one who was famed for the number of
      things
   He forgot when he entered the ship:
His umbrella, his watch, all his jewels and rings,
   And the clothes he had bought for the trip.

He had forty-two boxes, all carefully packed,
   With his name painted clearly on each:
But, since he omitted to mention the fact,
   They were all left behind on the beach.

The loss of his clothes hardly mattered, because
   He had seven coats on when he came,
With three pair of boots—but the worst of it was,
   He had wholly forgotten his name.

He would answer to 'Hi!' or to any loud cry,
   Such as 'Fry me!' or 'Fritter my wig!'
To 'What-you-may-call-um!' or 'What-was-his
      name!'
   But especially 'Thing-um-a-jig!'

While, for those who preferred a more forcible word,
   He had different names from these:
His intimate friends called him 'Candle-ends,'
   And his enemies 'Toasted-cheese.'

'His form is ungainly—his intellect small——'
   (So the Bellman would often remark)
'But his courage is perfect!   And that, after all,
   Is the thing that one needs with a Snark.'

He would joke with hyænas, returning their stare
   With an impudent wag of the head:
And he once went a walk, paw-in-paw, with a bear,
   'Just to keep up its spirits,' he said.

He came as a Baker: but owned when too late—
   And it drove the poor Bellman half mad—
He could only bake Bridecake—for which, I may state,
   No materials were to be had.

The last of the crew needs especial remark,
   Though he looked an incredible dunce:
He had just one idea—but, that one being 'Snark,'
   The good Bellman engaged him at once.

He came as a Butcher: but gravely declared,
   When the ship had been sailing a week,
He could only kill Beavers.   The Bellman looked
      scared,
   And was almost too frightened to speak:

But at length he explained, in a tremulous tone,
   There was only one Beaver on board;
And that was a tame one he had of his own,
   Whose death would be deeply deplored.

The Beaver, who happened to hear the remark,
   Protested, with tears in its eyes,
That not even the rapture of hunting the Snark
   Could atone for that dismal surprise!

It strongly advised that the Butcher should be
    Conveyed in a separate ship:
But the Bellman declared that would never agree
    With the plans he had made for the trip:

Navigation was always a difficult art,
    Though with only one ship and one bell:
And he feared he must really decline, for his part,
    Undertaking another as well.

The Beaver's best course was, no doubt, to procure
    A second-hand dagger-proof coat—
So the Baker advised it—and next, to insure
    Its life in some Office of note:

This the Banker suggested, and offered for hire
    (On moderate terms), or for sale,
Two excellent Policies, one Against Fire,
    And one Against Damage From Hail.

Yet still, ever after that sorrowful day,
    Whenever the Butcher was by,
The Beaver kept looking the opposite way,
    And appeared unaccountably shy.

FIT THE SECOND

The Bellman's Speech

The Bellman himself they all praised to the skies—
    Such a carriage, such ease and such grace!
Such solemnity, too!   One could see he was wise,
    The moment one looked in his face!

He had bought a large map representing the sea,
  Without the least vestige of land:
And the crew were much pleased when they found it
    to be
  A map they could all understand.

'What's the good of Mercator's North Poles and
    Equators,
  Tropics, Zones, and Meridian Lines?'
So the Bellman would cry: and the crew would
    reply
  'They are merely conventional signs!

'Other maps are such shapes, with their islands and
    capes!
  But we've got our brave Captain to thank!'
(So the crew would protest) 'that he's bought us the
    best—
  A perfect and absolute blank!'

This was charming, no doubt: but they shortly found
    out
  That the Captain they trusted so well
Had only one notion for crossing the ocean,
  And that was to tingle his bell.

He was thoughtful and grave—but the orders he
    gave
  Were enough to bewilder a crew.
When he cried 'Steer to starboard, but keep her head
    larboard!'
  What on earth was the helmsman to do?

Then the bowsprit got mixed with the rudder some-
    times:
    A thing, as the Bellman remarked,
That frequently happens in tropical climes,
    When a vessel is, so to speak, 'snarked.'

But the principal failing occurred in the sailing,
    And the Bellman, perplexed and distressed,
Said he *had* hoped, at least, when the wind blew due
    East
    That the ship would *not* travel due West!

But the danger was past—they had landed at last,
    With their boxes, portmanteaus, and bags:
Yet at first sight the crew were not pleased with the
    view,
    Which consisted of chasms and crags.

The Bellman perceived that their spirits were low,
    And repeated in musical tone
Some jokes he had kept for a season of woe—
    But the crew would do nothing but groan.

He served out some grog with a liberal hand,
    And bade them sit down on the beach:
And they could not but own that their Captain looked
    grand,
    As he stood and delivered his speech.

'Friends, Romans, countrymen, lend me your ears!'
    (They were all of them fond of quotations:
So they drank to his health, and they gave him three
    cheers,
    While he served out additional rations.)

'We have sailed many months, we have sailed many
    weeks
    (Four weeks to the month you may mark),
But never as yet ('tis your Captain who speaks)
    Have we caught the least glimpse of a Snark!

'We have sailed many weeks, we have sailed many
    days
    (Seven days to the week I allow),
But a Snark, on the which we might lovingly gaze,
    We have never beheld till now!

'Come, listen, my men, while I tell you again
    The five unmistakable marks
By which you may know, wheresoever you go,
    The warranted genuine Snarks.

'Let us take them in order. The first is the taste,
    Which is meagre and hollow, but crisp:
Like a coat that is rather too tight in the waist,
    With a flavour of Will-o'-the-wisp.

'Its habit of getting up late you'll agree
    That it carries too far, when I say
That it frequently breakfasts at five-o'clock tea,
    And dines on the following day.

'The third is its slowness in taking a jest,
    Should you happen to venture on one,
It will sigh like a thing that is deeply distressed:
    And it always looks grave at a pun.

'The fourth is its fondness for bathing-machines,
    Which it constantly carries about,
And believes that they add to the beauty of scenes—
    A sentiment open to doubt.

'The fifth is ambition.   It next will be right
    To describe each particular batch:
Distinguishing those that have feathers, and bite,
    From those that have whiskers, and scratch.

'For, although common Snarks do no manner of
        harm,
    Yet, I feel it my duty to say,
Some are Boojums——'   The Bellman broke off in
        alarm,
    For the Baker had fainted away.

FIT THE THIRD

The Baker's Tale

They roused him with muffins—they roused him
        with ice—
    They roused him with mustard and cress—
They roused him with jam and judicious advice—
    They set him conundrums to guess.

When at length he sat up and was able to speak,
    His sad story he offered to tell;
And the Bellman cried 'Silence! not even a shriek!'
    And excitedly tingled his bell.

There was silence supreme! Not a shriek, not a
    scream,
    Scarcely even a howl or a groan,
As the man they called 'Ho!' told his story of woe
    In an antediluvian tone.

'My father and mother were honest, though poor——'
    'Skip all that!' cried the Bellman in haste.
'If it once becomes dark, there's no chance of a
    Snark——
    We have hardly a minute to waste!'

'I skip forty years,' said the Baker, in tears,
    'And proceed without further remark
To the day when you took me aboard of your ship
    To help you in hunting the Snark.

'A dear uncle of mine (after whom I was named)
    Remarked, when I bade him farewell——'
'Oh, skip your dear uncle!' the Bellman exclaimed,
    As he angrily tingled his bell.

'He remarked to me then,' said that mildest of men,
    '"If your Snark be a Snark, that is right:
Fetch it home by all means—you may serve it with
    greens,
    And it's handy for striking a light.

'"You may seek it with thimbles—and seek it with
    care;
    You may hunt it with forks and hope;
You may threaten its life with a railway-share;
    You may charm it with smiles and soap——"'

('That 's exactly the method,' the Bellman bold
　　In a hasty parenthesis cried,
'That 's exactly the way I have always been told
　　That the capture of Snarks should be tried!')

'"But oh, beamish nephew, beware of the day,
　　If your Snark be a Boojum!　For then
You will softly and suddenly vanish away,
　　And never be met with again!"

'It is this, it is this that oppresses my soul,
　　When I think of my uncle's last words:
And my heart is like nothing so much as a bowl
　　Brimming over with quivering curds!

'It is this, it is this——'　'We have had that before!'
　　The Bellman indignantly said.
And the Baker replied 'Let me say it once more.
　　It is this, it is this that I dread!

'I engage with the Snark—every night after dark—
　　In a dreamy delirious fight:
I serve it with greens in those shadowy scenes,
　　And I use it for striking a light;

'But if ever I meet with a Boojum, that day,
　　In a moment (of this I am sure),
I shall softly and suddenly vanish away—
　　And the notion I cannot endure!'

FIT THE FOURTH

The Hunting

The Bellman looked uffish, and wrinkled his brow.
  'If only you 'd spoken before!
'It 's excessively awkward to mention it now,
  With the Snark, so to speak, at the door!

'We should all of us grieve, as you well may believe,
  If you never were met with again——
But surely, my man, when the voyage began,
  You might have suggested it then?

'It 's excessively awkward to mention it now—
  As I think I 've already remarked.'
And the man they called 'Hi!' replied, with a sigh,
  'I informed you the day we embarked.

'You may charge me with murder—or want of sense—
  (We are all of us weak at times):
But the slightest approach to a false pretence
  Was never among my crimes!

'I said it in Hebrew—I said it in Dutch—
  I said it in German and Greek;
But I wholly forgot (and it vexes me much)
  That English is what you speak!'

''Tis a pitiful tale,' said the Bellman, whose face
  Had grown longer at every word;
'But, now that you 've stated the whole of your case,
  More debate would be simply absurd.

'The rest of my speech' (he explained to his men)
   'You shall hear when I 've leisure to speak it.
But the Snark is at hand, let me tell you again!
   'Tis your glorious duty to seek it!

'To seek it with thimbles, to seek it with care;
   To pursue it with forks and hope;
To threaten its life with a railway-share;
   To charm it with smiles and soap!

'For the Snark 's a peculiar creature, that won't
   Be caught in a commonplace way.
Do all that you know, and try all that you don't:
   Not a chance must be wasted to-day!

'For England expects—I forbear to proceed:
   'Tis a maxim tremendous, but trite:
And you 'd best be unpacking the things that you
     need
   To rig yourselves out for the fight.'

Then the Banker endorsed a blank cheque (which he
     crossed),
   And changed his loose silver for notes.
The Baker with care combed his whiskers and hair,
   And shook the dust out of his coats.

The Boots and the Broker were sharpening a spade—
   Each working the grindstone in turn;
But the Beaver went on making lace, and displayed
   No interest in the concern:

'*To pursue it with forks and hope . . .*'

Though the Barrister tried to appeal to its pride,
    And vainly proceeded to cite
A number of cases, in which making laces
    Had been proved an infringement of right.

The maker of Bonnets ferociously planned
    A novel arrangement of bows:
While the Billiard-marker with quivering hand
    Was chalking the tip of his nose.

But the Butcher turned nervous, and dressed himself
        fine,
    With yellow kid gloves and a ruff—
Said he felt it exactly like going to dine,
    Which the Bellman declared was all 'stuff.'

'Introduce me, now there's a good fellow,' he said,
    'If we happen to meet it together!'
And the Bellman, sagaciously nodding his head,
    Said 'That must depend on the weather.'

The Beaver went simply galumphing about,
    At seeing the Butcher so shy:
And even the Baker, though stupid and stout,
    Made an effort to wink with one eye.

'Be a man!' said the Bellman in wrath, as he heard
    The Butcher beginning to sob.
'Should we meet with a Jubjub, that desperate bird,
    We shall need all our strength for the job!'

FIT THE FIFTH

The Beaver's Lesson

They sought it with thimbles, they sought it with care;
  They pursued it with forks and hope;
They threatened its life with a railway-share;
  They charmed it with smiles and soap.

Then the Butcher contrived an ingenious plan
  For making a separate sally;
And had fixed on a spot unfrequented by man,
  A dismal and desolate valley.

But the very same plan to the Beaver occurred:
  It had chosen the very same place;
Yet neither betrayed, by a sign or a word,
  The disgust that appeared in his face.

Each thought he was thinking of nothing but 'Snark'
  And the glorious work of the day;
And each tried to pretend that he did not remark
  That the other was going that way.

But the valley grew narrow and narrower still,
  And the evening got darker and colder,
Till (merely from nervousness, not from goodwill)
  They marched along shoulder to shoulder.

Then a scream, shrill and high, rent the shuddering
    sky,
  And they knew that some danger was near:
The Beaver turned pale to the tip of its tail,
  And even the Butcher felt queer.

He thought of his childhood, left far far behind—
　　That blissful and innocent state—
The sound so exactly recalled to his mind
　　A pencil that squeaks on a slate!

''Tis the voice of the Jubjub!' he suddenly cried.
　　(This man, that they used to call 'Dunce.')
'As the Bellman would tell you,' he added with pride,
　　'I have uttered that sentiment once.

''Tis the note of the Jubjub!　Keep count, I entreat;
　　You will find I have told it you twice.
'Tis the song of the Jubjub!　The proof is complete,
　　If only I 've stated it thrice.'

The Beaver had counted with scrupulous care,
　　Attending to every word:
But it fairly lost heart, and outgrabe in despair,
　　When the third repetition occurred.

It felt that, in spite of all possible pains,
　　It had somehow contrived to lose count,
And the only thing now was to rack its poor brains
　　By reckoning up the amount.

'Two added to one—if that could but be done,'
　　It said, 'with one's fingers and thumbs!'
Recollecting with tears how, in earlier years,
　　It had taken no pains with its sums.

'The thing can be done,' said the Butcher, 'I think.
　　The thing must be done, I am sure.
The thing shall be done!　Bring me paper and ink,
　　The best there is time to procure.'

The Beaver brought paper, portfolio, pens,
  And ink in unfailing supplies:
While strange creepy creatures came out of their dens,
  And watched them with wondering eyes.

So engrossed was the Butcher, he heeded them not,
  As he wrote with a pen in each hand,
And explained all the while in a popular style
  Which the Beaver could well understand.

'Taking Three as the subject to reason about—
  A convenient number to state—
We add Seven, and Ten, and then multiply out
  By One Thousand diminished by Eight.

'The result we proceed to divide, as you see,
  By Nine Hundred and Ninety and Two:
Then subtract Seventeen, and the answer must be
  Exactly and perfectly true.

'The method employed I would gladly explain,
  While I have it so clear in my head,
If I had but the time and you had but the brain—
  But much yet remains to be said.

'In one moment I 've seen what has hitherto been
  Enveloped in absolute mystery,
And without extra charge I will give you at large
  A Lesson in Natural History.'

In his genial way he proceeded to say
  (Forgetting all laws of propriety,
And that giving instruction, without introduction,
  Would have caused quite a thrill in Society),

The Beaver brought paper, portfolio, pens

'As to temper the Jubjub's a desperate bird,
  Since it lives in perpetual passion:
Its taste in costume is entirely absurd—
  It is ages ahead of the fashion:

'But it knows any friend it has met once before:
  It never will look at a bribe:
And in charity meetings it stands at the door,
  And collects—though it does not subscribe.

'Its flavour when cooked is more exquisite far
  Than mutton, or oysters, or eggs:
(Some think it keeps best in an ivory jar,
  And some, in mahogany kegs:)

'You boil it in sawdust: you salt it in glue:
  You condense it with locusts and tape:
Still keeping one principal object in view—
  To preserve its symmetrical shape.'

The Butcher would gladly have talked till next day,
  But he felt that the Lesson must end,
And he wept with delight in attempting to say
  He considered the Beaver his friend.

While the Beaver confessed, with affectionate looks
  More eloquent even than tears,
It had learnt in ten minutes far more than all books
  Would have taught it in seventy years.

They returned **hand-in-hand**, and the Bellman, unmanned
  (For a moment) with noble emotion,
Said 'This amply repays all the wearisome days
  We have spent on the billowy ocean!'

Such friends, as the Beaver and Butcher became,
    Have seldom if ever been known;
In winter or summer, 'twas always the same—
    You could never meet either alone.

And when quarrels arose—as one frequently finds
    Quarrels will, spite of every endeavour—
The song of the Jubjub recurred to their minds,
    And cemented their friendship for ever!

FIT THE SIXTH

The Barrister's Dream

They sought it with thimbles, they sought it with care;
    They pursued it with forks and hope;
They threatened its life with a railway-share;
    They charmed it with smiles and soap.

But the Barrister, weary of proving in vain
    That the Beaver's lace-making was wrong,
Fell asleep, and in dreams saw the creature quite plain
    That his fancy had dwelt on so long.

He dreamed that he stood in a shadowy Court,
    Where the Snark, with a glass in its eye,
Dressed in gown, bands, and wig, was defending a pig
    On the charge of deserting its sty.

The Witnesses proved, without error or flaw,
    That the sty was deserted when found:
And the Judge kept explaining the state of the law
    In a soft undercurrent of sound.

The indictment had never been clearly expressed,
  And it seemed that the Snark had begun,
. And had spoken three hours, before anyone guessed
  What the pig was supposed to have done.

The Jury had each formed a different view
  (Long before the indictment was read),
And they all spoke at once, so that none of them knew
  One word that the others had said.

'You must know——' said the Judge: but Snark exclaimed 'Fudge!
  That statute is obsolete quite!
Let me tell you, my friends, the whole question depends
  On an ancient manorial right.

'In the matter of Treason the pig would appear
  To have aided, but scarcely abetted:
While the charge of Insolvency, fails, it is clear,
  If you grant the plea "never indebted."

'The fact of Desertion I will not dispute:
  But its guilt, as I trust, is removed
(So far as relates to the costs of this suit)
  By the Alibi which has been proved.

'My poor client's fate now depends on your votes.'
  Here the speaker sat down in his place,
And directed the Judge to refer to his notes
  And briefly to sum up the case.

But the Judge said he never had summed up before;
  So the Snark undertook it instead,
And summed it so well that it came to far more
  Than the Witnesses ever had said!

When the verdict was called for, the Jury declined,
  As the word was so puzzling to spell;
But they ventured to hope that the Snark wouldn't
  mind
  Undertaking that duty as well.

So the Snark found the verdict, although, as it owned,
  It was spent with the toils of the day:
When it said the word 'GUILTY!' the Jury all
  groaned,
  And some of them fainted away.

Then the Snark pronounced sentence, the Judge
  being quite
  Too nervous to utter a word:
When it rose to its feet, there was silence like night,
  And the fall of a pin might be heard.

'Transportation for life' was the sentence it gave,
  'And *then* to be fined forty pound.'
The Jury all cheered, though the Judge said he
  feared
  That the phrase was not legally sound.

But their wild exultation was suddenly checked
  When the jailer informed them, with tears,
Such a sentence would have not the slightest effect,
  As the pig had been dead for some years.

The Judge left the Court, looking deeply disgusted:
    But the Snark, though a little aghast,
As the lawyer to whom the defence was intrusted,
    Went bellowing on to the last.

Thus the Barrister dreamed, while the bellowing
    seemed
    To grow every moment more clear:
Till he woke to the knell of a furious bell,
    Which the Bellman rang close at his ear.

FIT THE SEVENTH

The Banker's Fate

They sought it with thimbles, they sought it with care;
    They pursued it with forks and hope;
They threatened its life with a railway-share;
    They charmed it with smiles and soap.

And the Banker, inspired with a courage so new
    It was matter for general remark,
Rushed madly ahead and was lost to their view
    In his zeal to discover the Snark.

But while he was seeking with thimbles and care,
    A Bandersnatch swiftly drew nigh
And grabbed at the Banker, who shrieked in despair,
    For he knew it was useless to fly.

He offered large discount—he offered a cheque
    (Drawn 'to bearer') for seven-pounds-ten:
But the Bandersnatch merely extended its neck
    And grabbed at the Banker again.

Without rest or pause—while those frumious jaws
    Went savagely snapping around—
He skipped and he hopped, and he floundered and
    flopped,
    Till fainting he fell to the ground.

The Bandersnatch fled as the others appeared:
    Led on by that fear-stricken yell:
And the Bellman remarked 'It is just as I feared!'
    And solemnly tolled on his bell.

He was black in the face, and they scarcely could
    trace
    The least likeness to what he had been:
While so great was his fright that his waistcoat turned
    white—
    A wonderful thing to be seen!

To the horror of all who were present that day,
    He uprose in full evening dress,
And with senseless grimaces endeavoured to say
    What his tongue could no longer express.

Down he sank in a chair—ran his hands through his
    hair—
    And chanted in mimsiest tones
Words whose utter inanity proved his insanity,
    While he rattled a couple of bones.

'Leave him here to his fate—it is getting so late!'
    The Bellman exclaimed in a fright.
'We have lost half the day.   Any further delay,
    And we sha'n't catch a Snark before night!'

FIT THE EIGHTH

The Vanishing

They sought it with thimbles, they sought it with care;
    They pursued it with forks and hope;
They threatened its life with a railway-share;
    They charmed it with smiles and soap.

They shuddered to think that the chase might fail,
    And the Beaver, excited at last,
Went bounding along on the tip of its tail,
    For the daylight was nearly past.

'There is Thingumbob shouting!' the Bellman said.
    'He is shouting like mad, only hark!
He is waving his hands, he is wagging his head,
    He has certainly found a Snark!'

They gazed in delight, while the Butcher exclaimed
    'He was always a desperate wag!'
They beheld him—their Baker—their hero unnamed—
    On the top of a neighbouring crag,

Erect and sublime, for one moment of time.
    In the next, that wild figure they saw
(As if stung by a spasm) plunge into a chasm,
    While they waited and listened in awe.

'It 's a Snark!' was the sound that first came to their
      ears,
    And seemed almost too good to be true.
Then followed a torrent of laughter and cheers:
    Then the ominous words 'It 's a Boo——'

Then, silence.   Some fancied they heard in the air
    A weary and wandering sigh
That sounded like '—jum!' but the others declare
    It was only a breeze that went by.

They hunted till darkness came on, but they found
    Not a button, or feather, or mark,
By which they could tell that they stood on the ground
    Where the Baker had met with the Snark.

In the midst of the word he was trying to say,
    In the midst of his laughter and glee,
He had softly and suddenly vanished away—
    For the Snark *was* a Boojum, you see.

                                    (1876.)

THE STORY OF THE FOUR LITTLE CHILDREN WHO WENT ROUND THE WORLD

By EDWARD LEAR

ONCE upon a time, a long while ago, there were four little people whose names were :

VIOLET, SLINGSBY, GUY, and LIONEL;

and they all thought they should like to see the world. So they bought a large boat to sail quite round the world by sea, and then they were to come back on the other side by land. The boat was painted blue with green spots, and the sail was yellow with red stripes; and when they set off, they only took a small cat to steer and look after the boat, besides

29

an elderly quangle-wangle, who had to cook the dinner and make the tea; for which purposes they took a large kettle.

For the first ten days they sailed on beautifully, and found

plenty to eat, as there were lots of fish, and they had only to take them out of the sea with a long spoon, when the quangle-wangle instantly cooked them, and the pussy-cat was fed with the bones, with which she expressed herself pleased on the whole, so that all the party were very happy.

During the day-time, Violet chiefly occupied herself in putting salt-water into a churn, while her three brothers churned it violently, in the hope that it would turn into butter, which it seldom if ever did; and in the evening they all retired into the tea-kettle, where they all managed to sleep

very comfortably, while Pussy and the quangle-wangle managed the boat.

After a time they saw some land at a distance; and when they came to it they found it was an island made of water quite surrounded by earth. Besides that, it was bordered by evanescent isthmuses with a great Gulf-stream running about all over it, so that it was perfectly beautiful, and contained only a single tree, 503 feet high.

When they had landed, they walked about, but found to their great surprise that the island was quite full of veal-cutlets and chocolate-drops, and nothing else. So they all climbed up the single high tree to discover, if possible, if there were any people; but having remained on the top of the tree for a week and not seeing anybody, they naturally concluded that there were no inhabitants, and accordingly when they came down they loaded the boat with two thousand veal-cutlets and a million of chocolate drops, and these afforded them sustenance for more than a month, during

which time they pursued their voyage with the utmost
delight and apathy.

After this they came to a shore where there were no less

than sixty-five great red parrots with blue tails, sitting on a
rail all of a row, and all fast asleep.   And I am sorry to say
that the pussy-cat and the quangle-wangle crept softly and

bit off the tail-feathers of all the sixty-five parrots, for which
Violet reproved them both severely.

Notwithstanding which, she proceeded to insert all the
feathers, two hundred and sixty in number, in her bonnet,

thereby causing it to have a lovely and glittering appearance, highly prepossessing and efficacious.

The next thing that happened to them was in a narrow part of the sea, which was so entirely full of fishes that the boat could go no farther; so they remained there about six weeks, till they had eaten nearly all the fishes, which were soles, and all ready-cooked and covered with shrimp sauce, so that there was no trouble whatever.   And as the few fishes who remained uneaten complained of the cold, as well

as of the difficulty they had in getting any sleep on account of the extreme noise made by the arctic bears and the tropical turnspits, which frequented the neighbourhood in great numbers, Violet most amiably knitted a small woollen frock for several of the fishes, and Slingsby administered some opium drops to them, through which kindness they became quite warm and slept soundly.

Then they came to a country which was wholly covered with immense orange-trees of a vast size, and quite full of fruit.   So they all landed, taking with them the tea-kettle, intending to gather some of the oranges and place them in it.   But while they were busy about this, a most dreadfully high wind rose, and blew out most of the parrot tail-feathers

from Violet's bonnet. That, however, was nothing com-
pared with the calamity of the oranges falling down on their
heads by millions and millions, which thumped and bumped
and bumped and thumped them all so seriously that they

were obliged to run as hard as they could for their lives,
besides that the sound of the oranges rattling on the tea-
kettle was of the most fearful and amazing nature.

Nevertheless they got safely to the boat, although con-
siderably vexed and hurt; and the quangle-wangle's right

foot was so knocked about that he had to sit with his head in
his slipper for at least a week.

This event made them all for a time rather melancholy,
and perhaps they might never have become less so, had not
Lionel, with a most praiseworthy devotion and perseverance,

continued to stand on one leg and whistle to them in a loud and lively manner, which diverted the whole party so extremely, that they gradually recovered their spirits, and agreed that whenever they should reach home they would subscribe towards a testimony to Lionel, entirely made of gingerbread and raspberries, as an earnest token of their sincere and grateful infection.

After sailing on calmly for several more days, they came to another country, where they were much pleased and surprised to see a countless multitude of white mice with red eyes, all sitting in a great circle, slowly eating custard pudding with the most satisfactory and polite demeanour.

And as the four travellers were rather hungry, being tired of eating nothing but soles and oranges for so long a period, they held a council as to the propriety of asking the mice for some of their pudding in a humble and affecting manner, by

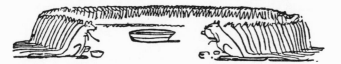

which they could hardly be otherwise than gratified.   It was agreed therefore that Guy should go and ask the mice, which he immediately did; and the result was that they gave a walnut-shell only half full of custard diluted with water. Now, this displeased Guy, who said: 'Out of such a lot of pudding as you have got, I must say you might have spared a somewhat larger quantity!'   But no sooner had he finished

speaking than all the mice turned round at once, and sneezed
at him in an appalling and vindictive manner (and it is im-
possible to imagine a more scroobious and unpleasant sound
than that caused by the simultaneous sneezing of many
millions of angry mice), so that Guy rushed back to the boat,

having first shied his cap into the middle of the custard
pudding, by which means he completely spoiled the mice's
dinner.

By and by the four children came to a country where there
were no houses, but only an incredibly innumerable number
of large bottles without corks, and of a dazzling and sweetly
susceptible blue colour.   Each of these blue bottles contained a bluebottle fly, and all these interesting animals live

continually together in the most copious and rural harmony,
nor perhaps in many parts of the world is such perfect and
abject happiness to be found.   Violet, and Slingsby, and
Guy, and Lionel were greatly struck with this singular and
instructive settlement, and having previously asked permission of the bluebottle flies (which was most courteously

granted), the boat was drawn up to the shore, and they proceeded to make tea in front of the bottles; but as they had no
tea-leaves, they merely placed some pebbles in the hot
water, and the quangle-wangle played some tunes over it on
an accordion, by which of course tea was made directly, and
of the very best quality.

The four children then entered into conversation with the
bluebottle flies, who discoursed in a placid and genteel
manner, though with a slightly buzzing accent, chiefly
owing to the fact that they each held a small clothes-brush
between their teeth, which naturally occasioned a fizzy
extraneous utterance.

'Why,' said Violet, 'would you kindly inform us, do you
reside in bottles, and if in bottles at all, why not rather in
green or purple, or indeed in yellow bottles?'

To which questions a very aged bluebottle fly answered:
'We found the bottles here all ready to live in, that is to say,
our great-great-great-great-great-grandfathers did, so we
occupied them at once. And when the winter comes on,
we turn the bottles upside-down, and consequently rarely
feel the cold at all, and you know very well that this could not
be the case with bottles of any other colour than blue.'

'Of course it could not,' said Slingsby; 'but if we may
take the liberty of inquiring, on what do you chiefly subsist?'

'Mainly on oyster-patties,' said the bluebottle fly, 'and
when these are scarce, on raspberry vinegar and Russian
leather boiled down to a jelly.'

'How delicious!' said Guy.

To which Lionel added, 'Huzz!' and all the bluebottle
flies said 'Buzz!'

At this time, an elderly fly said it was the hour for the
evening-song to be sung; and on a signal being given all the
bluebottle flies began to buzz at once in a sumptuous and

sonorous manner, the melodious and mucilaginous sounds echoing all over the waters, and resounding across the tumultuous tops of the transitory titmice upon the intervening and verdant mountains, with a serene and sickly suavity only known to the truly virtuous.   The moon was shining slobaciously from the star-bespangled sky, while her light irrigated the smooth and shiny sides and wings and backs of the bluebottle flies with a peculiar and trivial splendour, while all nature cheerfully responded to the cerulean and conspicuous circumstances.

In many long-after years, the four little travellers looked back to that evening as one of the happiest in all their lives, and it was already past midnight, when—the sail of the boat having been set up by the quangle-wangle, the tea-kettle and churn placed in their respective positions, and the pussy-cat stationed at the helm—the children each took a last and affectionate farewell of the bluebottle flies, who walked down in a body to the water's edge to see the travellers embark.

As a token of parting respect and esteem, Violet made a curtsy quite down to the ground, and stuck one of her few remaining parrot tail-feathers into the back hair of the most pleasing of the bluebottle flies, while Slingsby, Guy, and Lionel offered them three small boxes, containing respectively black pins, dried figs, and Epsom salts; and thus they left that happy shore for ever.

Overcome by their feelings, the four little travellers instantly jumped into the tea-kettle, and fell fast asleep.   But all along the shore for many hours there was distinctly heard a sound of severely suppressed sobs, and a vague multitude of living creatures using their pocket-handkerchiefs in a subdued simultaneous snuffle—lingering sadly along the wallopping waves, as the boat sailed farther and farther away from the land of the happy bluebottle flies.

Nothing particular occurred for some days after these events, except that as the travellers were passing a low tract of sand, they perceived an unusual and gratifying spectacle, namely, a large number of crabs and crawfish—perhaps six or seven hundred—sitting by the waterside, and endeavouring to disentangle a vast heap of pale pink worsted, which they moistened at intervals with a fluid composed of Lavender-water and White-wine Negus.

'Can we be of any service to you, O crusty Crabbies?' said the four children.

'Thank you kindly,' said the crabs consecutively. 'We are trying to make some worsted mittens, but do not know how.'

On which Violet, who was perfectly acquainted with the art of mitten-making, said to the crabs: 'Do your claws unscrew, or are they fixtures?'

'They are all made to unscrew,' said the crabs, and forthwith they deposited a great pile of claws close to the boat, with which Violet uncombed all the pale pink worsted, and then made the loveliest mittens with it you can imagine. These the crabs, having resumed and screwed on their claws, placed cheerfully upon their wrists, and walked away rapidly, on their hind legs, warbling songs with a silvery voice and in a minor key.

After this the four little people sailed on again till they came to a vast and wide plain of astonishing dimensions, on which nothing whatever could be discovered at first; but as the travellers walked onward, there appeared in the extreme and dim distance a single object, which on a nearer approach, and on an accurately cutaneous inspection, seemed to be somebody in a large white wig sitting on an arm-chair made of sponge cakes and oyster-shells. 'It does not quite look like a human being,' said Violet doubtfully; nor could they make out what it really was, till the quangle-wangle (who had

previously been round the world) exclaimed softly in a loud voice: 'It is the co-operative cauliflower!'

And so in truth it was, and they soon found that what they had taken for an immense wig was in reality the top of the cauliflower, and that he had no feet at all, being able to walk tolerably well with a fluctuating and graceful movement on a single cabbage stalk, an accomplishment which naturally saved him the expense of stockings and shoes.

Presently, while the whole party from the boat was gazing at him with mingled affection and disgust, he suddenly arose, and in a somewhat plumdomphious manner hurried off towards the setting sun—his steps supported by two superincumbent confidential cucumbers, and a large number of waterwagtails proceeding in advance of him by three-and-three in a row—till he finally disappeared on the brink of the western sky in a crystal cloud of sudorific sand.

e they were received by their admiring rela-
tempered with contempt; and where they
d to carry out the rest of their travelling plans
avourable opportunity.

hinoceros, in token of their grateful adherence,
killed and stuffed directly, and then set him up
oor of their father's house as a diaphanous

(Written 1866; published 1871.)

So remarkable a sight of course impressed the four children very deeply; and they returned immediately to their boat
with a strong sense of undeveloped asthma and a great
appetite.

Shortly after this the travellers were obliged to sail directly

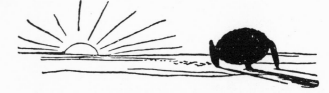

below some high overhanging rocks, from the top of one of
which a particularly odious little boy, dressed in rose-
coloured knickerbockers, and with a pewter plate upon his
head, threw an enormous pumpkin at the boat, by which it
was instantly upset.

But this upsetting was of no consequence, because all the
party knew how to swim very well, and in fact they preferred
swimming about till after the moon rose, when, the water
growing chilly, they sponge-taneously entered the boat.

Meanwhile the quangle-wangle threw back the pumpkin with immense force, so that it hit the rocks where the malicious little boy in rose-coloured knickerbockers was sitting, when, being quite full of Lucifer-matches, the pumpkin exploded surreptitiously into a thousand bits, whereon the rocks instantly took fire, and the odious little boy became unpleasantly hotter and hotter and hotter, till his knickerbockers were turned quite green, and his nose was burned off.

Two or three days after this had happened they came to another place, where they found nothing at all except some wide and deep pits full of mulberry jam. This is the property of the tiny yellow-nosed apes who abound in these districts, and who store up the mulberry jam for their food in winter, when they mix it with pellucid pale periwinkle soup, and serve it out in Wedgwood china bowls, which grow freely all over that part of the country. Only one of the yellow-nosed apes was on the spot, and he was fast asleep; yet the four travellers and the quangle-wangle and pussy were so terrified by the violence and sanguinary sound of his snoring, that they merely took a small cupful of the jam, and returned to re-embark in their boat without delay.

What was their horror on seeing the boat (including the churn and the tea-kettle) in the mouth of an enormous seeze pyder, an aquatic and ferocious creature truly dreadful to behold, and happily only met with in those excessive longitudes. In a moment the beautiful boat was bitten into fifty-five-thousand-million-hundred-billion bits; and it instantly became quite clear that Violet, Slingsby, Guy, and Lionel could no longer preliminate their voyage by sea.

The four travellers were therefore obliged to resolve on pursuing their wanderings by land, and very fortunately there happened to pass by at that moment an elderly rhinoceros, on which they seized; and all four mounting on his

back, the quangle-wan
on by his ears, and the
tail, they set off, havin
pounds of mashed po
journey.

at home,
tives wit.
finally res
at some n
As for
they had
outside t
door-scra

They were, however,
and turkeys and other
head of the rhinoceros f
of the rhododendron
creatures they cooked
factory manner, by me

rhinoceros's back. A
cranes accompanied th
complacency, so that th
and went onward as it
phant procession.
Thus, in less than e

So remarkable a sight of course impressed the four children very deeply; and they returned immediately to their boat with a strong sense of undeveloped asthma and a great appetite.

Shortly after this the travellers were obliged to sail directly

below some high overhanging rocks, from the top of one of which a particularly odious little boy, dressed in rose-coloured knickerbockers, and with a pewter plate upon his head, threw an enormous pumpkin at the boat, by which it was instantly upset.

But this upsetting was of no consequence, because all the party knew how to swim very well, and in fact they preferred swimming about till after the moon rose, when, the water growing chilly, they sponge-taneously entered the boat.

Meanwhile the quangle-wangle threw back the pumpkin with immense force, so that it hit the rocks where the malicious little boy in rose-coloured knickerbockers was sitting, when, being quite full of Lucifer-matches, the pumpkin exploded surreptitiously into a thousand bits, whereon the rocks instantly took fire, and the odious little boy became unpleasantly hotter and hotter and hotter, till his knickerbockers were turned quite green, and his nose was burned off.

Two or three days after this had happened they came to another place, where they found nothing at all except some wide and deep pits full of mulberry jam. This is the property of the tiny yellow-nosed apes who abound in these districts, and who store up the mulberry jam for their food in winter, when they mix it with pellucid pale periwinkle soup, and serve it out in Wedgwood china bowls, which grow freely all over that part of the country. Only one of the yellow-nosed apes was on the spot, and he was fast asleep; yet the four travellers and the quangle-wangle and pussy were so terrified by the violence and sanguinary sound of his snoring, that they merely took a small cupful of the jam, and returned to re-embark in their boat without delay.

What was their horror on seeing the boat (including the churn and the tea-kettle) in the mouth of an enormous seeze pyder, an aquatic and ferocious creature truly dreadful to behold, and happily only met with in those excessive longitudes. In a moment the beautiful boat was bitten into fifty-five-thousand-million-hundred-billion bits; and it instantly became quite clear that Violet, Slingsby, Guy, and Lionel could no longer preliminate their voyage by sea.

The four travellers were therefore obliged to resolve on pursuing their wanderings by land, and very fortunately there happened to pass by at that moment an elderly rhinoceros, on which they seized; and all four mounting on his back, the quangle-wangle sitting on his horn and holding on by his ears, and the pussy-cat swinging at the end of his tail, they set off, having only four small beans and three pounds of mashed potatoes to last through their whole journey.

They were, however, able to catch numbers of the chickens and turkeys and other birds who incessantly alighted on the head of the rhinoceros for the purpose of gathering the seeds of the rhododendron plants which grew there, and these creatures they cooked in the most translucent and satisfactory manner, by means of a fire lighted on the end of the

rhinoceros's back.   A crowd of kangaroos and gigantic cranes accompanied them, from feelings of curiosity and complacency, so that they were never at a loss for company, and went onward as it were in a sort of profuse and triumphant procession.

Thus, in less than eighteen weeks, they all arrived safely

at home, where they were received by their admiring relatives with joy tempered with contempt; and where they finally resolved to carry out the rest of their travelling plans at some more favourable opportunity.

As for the rhinoceros, in token of their grateful adherence, they had him killed and stuffed directly, and then set him up outside the door of their father's house as a diaphanous door-scraper.

(Written 1866; published 1871.)

II

THE LOBSTER

'Tis the voice of the Lobster; I heard him declare,
'You have baked me too brown, I must sugar my hair.'
As a duck with its eyelids, so he with his nose
Trims his belt and his buttons, and turns out his toes.

I passed by his garden, and marked with one eye,
How the Owl and the Oyster were sharing a pie;
While the Duck and the Dodo, the Lizard and Cat
Were swimming in milk round the brim of a hat.

(1865 and 1870.)

III

DOLLY'S DOGS

'Will you trot a little quicker?' said a Lily to a Fox.
'It 's gone eleven half an hour by all the village clocks:
And dinner-time is twelve, you know, and Dolly *will* be
    wrath,
If we 're not there to carry round the plates of mutton-broth.'

'Don't talk to me of going quick,' said Fox, 'you howling
    Hound!
My feet are done with patent glue, that sticks them to the
    ground.
It is my own invention—so Dolly needn't scold:
She can't invent a patent glue that 's worth its weight in
    gold!'

(1868.)

IV

THE WALRUS AND THE CARPENTER

The sun was shining on the sea,
    Shining with all his might:
He did his very best to make
    The billows smooth and bright—
And this was odd, because it was
    The middle of the night.

The moon was shining sulkily,
    Because she thought the sun
Had got no business to be there
    After the day was done—
'It's very rude of him,' she said,
    'To come and spoil the fun!'

The sea was wet as wet could be,
    The sands were dry as dry.
You could not see a cloud, because
    No cloud was in the sky:
No birds were flying overhead—
    There were no birds to fly.

The Walrus and the Carpenter
    Were walking close at hand;
They wept like anything to see
    Such quantities of sand:
'If this were only cleared away,'
    They said, 'it *would* be grand!'

'If seven maids with seven mops
    Swept it for half a year,
Do you suppose,' the Walrus said,
    'That they could get it clear?'
'I doubt it,' said the Carpenter,
    And shed a bitter tear.

'O Oysters, come and walk with us!'
    The Walrus did beseech.
'A pleasant walk, a pleasant talk,
    Along the briny beach:
We cannot do with more than four,
    To give a hand to each.'

The eldest Oyster looked at him,
    But never a word he said:
The eldest Oyster winked his eye,
    And shook his heavy head—
Meaning to say he did not choose
    To leave the oyster-bed.

But four young Oysters hurried up,
    All eager for the treat:
Their coats were brushed, their faces washed,
    Their shoes were clean and neat—
And this was odd, because, you know,
    They hadn't any feet.

Four other Oysters followed them,
    And yet another four;
And thick and fast they came at last,
    And more, and more, and more—
All hopping through the frothy waves,
    And scrambling to the shore.

The Walrus and the Carpenter
    Walked on a mile or so,
And then they rested on a rock
    Conveniently low:
And all the little Oysters stood
    And waited in a row.

'The time has come,' the Walrus said,
    'To talk of many things:
Of shoes—and ships—and sealing-wax—
    Of cabbages—and kings—
And why the sea is boiling hot—
    And whether pigs have wings.'

'But wait a bit,' the Oysters cried,
    'Before we have our chat;
For some of us are out of breath,
    And all of us are fat!'
'No hurry!' said the Carpenter.
    They thanked him much for that.

'A loaf of bread,' the Walrus said,
    'Is what we chiefly need:
Pepper and vinegar besides
    Are very good indeed—
Now if you 're ready, Oysters dear,
    We can begin to feed.'

'But not on us!' the Oysters cried,
    Turning a little blue.
'After such kindness, that would be
    A dismal thing to do!'
'The night is fine,' the Walrus said.
    'Do you admire the view?

'It was so kind of you to come!
    And you are very nice!'
The Carpenter said nothing but
    'Cut us another slice:
I wish you were not quite so deaf—
    I 've had to ask you twice!'

'It seems a shame,' the Walrus said,
    'To play them such a trick,
After we 've brought them out so far,
    And made them trot so quick!'
The Carpenter said nothing but
    'The butter 's spread too thick!'

'I weep for you,' the Walrus said:
    'I deeply sympathize.'
With sobs and tears he sorted out
    Those of the largest size,
Holding his pocket-handkerchief
    Before his streaming eyes.

'O Oysters,' said the Carpenter,
  'You 've had a pleasant run!
Shall we be trotting home again?'
  But answer came there none—
And this was scarcely odd, because
  They 'd eaten every one.

(1871.)

V

THE AGED, AGED MAN

I 'll tell thee everything I can;
   There 's little to relate.
I saw an aged, aged man,
   A-sitting on a gate.
'Who are you, aged man?' I said.
   'And how is it you live?'
And his answer trickled through my head
   Like water through a sieve.

He said: 'I look for butterflies
   That sleep among the wheat:
I make them into mutton-pies,
   And sell them in the street.

I weep, for it reminds me so
Of that old man I used to know—
Whose look was mild, whose speech was slow,
Whose hair was whiter than the snow,
Whose face was very like a crow,
With eyes, like cinders, all aglow,
Who seemed distracted with his woe,
Who rocked his body to and fro,
And muttered mumblingly and low,
As if his mouth were full of dough
Who snorted like a buffalo—
That summer evening long ago
    A-sitting on a gate.

                    (1856 and 1871.)

VI

THE MAD GARDENER'S SONG

He thought he saw an Elephant,
    That practised on a fife:
He looked again, and found it was
    A letter from his wife.
'At length I realize,' he said,
    'The bitterness of Life!'

He thought he saw a Buffalo
    Upon the chimney-piece:

He looked again, and found it was
His Sister's Husband's Niece.
'Unless you leave this house,' he said,
'I 'll send for the Police!'

He thought he saw a Rattlesnake
That questioned him in Greek:
He looked again, and found it was
The Middle of Next Week.
'The one thing I regret,' he said,
'Is that it cannot speak!'

He thought he saw a Banker's Clerk
Descending from the bus:

He looked again, and found it was
  A Hippopotamus:
'If this should stay to dine,' he said,
  'There won't be much for us!'

He thought he saw a Kangaroo
  That worked a coffee-mill:
He looked again, and found it was
  A Vegetable-Pill.
'Were I to swallow this,' he said,
  'I should be very ill!'

He thought he saw a Coach-and-Four
  That stood beside his bed:

He looked again, and found it was
   A Bear without a Head.
'Poor thing,' he said, 'poor silly thing!
   It 's waiting to be fed!'

He thought he saw an Albatross
   That fluttered round the lamp:
He looked again, and found it was
   A Penny-Postage-Stamp.
'You 'd best be getting home,' he said:
   'The nights are very damp!'

He thought he saw a Garden-Door
   That opened with a key:
He looked again, and found it was
   A Double Rule of Three:
'And all its mystery,' he said,
   'Is clear as day to me!'

He thought he saw an Argument
   That proved he was the Pope:

He looked again, and found it was
  A Bar of Mottled Soap.
'A fact so dread,' he faintly said,
  'Extinguishes all hope!'

(1889.)

VII

OUTLAND FARE

Oh, dear beyond our dearest dreams,
Fairer than all that fairest seems!
To feast the rosy hours away,
To revel in a roundelay!
  How blest would be
  A life so free—
Ipwergis-Pudding to consume,
And drink the subtle Azzigoom!

And if, in other days and hours,
Mid other fluffs and other flowers,
The choice were given me how to dine—
'Name what thou wilt; it shall be thine!'
  Oh, then I see
  The life for me—
Ipwergis-Pudding to consume,
And drink the subtle Azzigoom!

(1889.)

VIII

THE KING-FISHER SONG

King Fisher courted Lady Bird—
Sing Beans, sing Bones, sing Butterflies!
    'Find me my match,' he said,
    'With such a noble head—
With such a beard, as white as curd—
    With such expressive eyes!'

'Yet pins have heads,' said Lady Bird—
Sing Prunes, sing Prawns, sing Primrose-Hill!
 'And, where you stick them in,
 They stay, and thus a pin
*I*s very much to be preferred
 To one that's never still!'

'Oysters have beards,' said Lady Bird—
Sing Flies, sing Frogs, sing Fiddle-strings!
 'I love them, for I know
 They never chatter so:
They would not say one single word—
 Not if you crowned them Kings!'

'Needles have eyes,' said Lady Bird—
Sing Cats, sing Corks, sing Cowslip-tea!
 'And they are sharp—just what
 Your Majesty is *not:*
So get you gone—'tis too absurd
 To come a-courting *me*!'

        (1893.)

IX

THE PIG-TALE

There was a Pig that sat alone
 Beside a ruined Pump:
By day and night he made his moan—
It would have stirred a heart of stone
To see him wring his hoofs and groan,
 Because he could not jump.

A certain Camel heard him shout—
   A Camel with a hump.
'Oh, is it Grief, or is it Gout?
What is this bellowing about?'
That Pig replied, with quivering snout,
   'Because I cannot jump!'

That Camel scanned him, dreamy-eyed.
   'Methinks you are too plump.
I never knew a Pig so wide—
That wobbled so from side to side—
Who could, however much he tried,
   Do such a thing as *jump*!

'Yet mark those trees, two miles away,
   All clustered in a clump:
If you could trot there twice a day,
Nor ever pause for rest or play,
In the far future—who can say?—
   You may be fit to jump.'

That Camel passed, and left him there
   Beside the ruined Pump.
Oh, horrid was that Pig's despair!
His shrieks of anguish filled the air.
He wrung his hoofs, he rent his hair,
   Because he could not jump.

There was a Frog that wandered by—
   A sleek and shining lump:
Inspected him with fishy eye,
And said: 'O Pig, what makes you cry?'
And bitter was that Pig's reply,
   'Because I cannot jump!'

That Frog he grinned a grin of glee,
    And hit his chest a thump.
'O Pig,' he said, 'be ruled by me,
And you shall see what you shall see.
This minute, for a trifling fee,
    I 'll teach you how to jump!

'You may be faint from many a fall,
    And bruised by many a bump:
But, if you persevere through all,
And practise first on something small,
Concluding with a ten-foot wall,
    You 'll find that you *can* jump!'

That Pig looked up with joyful start:
    'Oh, Frog, you *are* a trump!
Your words have healed my inward smart—
Come, name your fee and do your part:
Bring comfort to a broken heart,
    By teaching me to jump!'

'My fee shall be a mutton-chop,
    My goal this ruined Pump.
Observe with what an airy flop
I plant myself upon the top!
Now bend your knees and take a hop,
    For that 's the way to jump!'

Uprose that Pig, and rushed, full whack,
    Against the ruined Pump:
Rolled over like an empty sack,
And settled down upon his back,
While all his bones at once went 'Crack!'
    It was a fatal jump.

That Camel passed, as day grew dim
    Around the ruined Pump.
'O broken heart! O broken limb!
It needs,' that Camel said to him,
'Something more fairy-like and slim,
    To execute a jump!'

That Pig lay still as any stone,
    And could not stir a stump:
Nor ever, if the truth were known,
Was he again observed to moan,
Nor ever wring his hoofs and groan,
    Because he could not jump.

That Frog made no remark, for he
　　Was dismal as a dump:
He knew the consequence must be
That he would never get his fee—
And still he sits, in miserie,
　　Upon that ruined Pump!

(1893.)

X

LITTLE BIRDS

Little Birds are dining
　　Warily and well
　　　Hid in mossy cell:
Hid, I say, by waiters
Gorgeous in their gaiters—
　　I 've a tale to tell.

Little Birds are seeking
　　Hecatombs of haws,
　　　Dressed in snowy gauze:
Dressed, I say, in fringes
Half alive with hinges—
　　　Thus they break the laws.

Little Birds are feeding
   Justices with jam,
     Rich with frizzled ham:
Rich, I say, in oysters
Haunting shady cloisters—
     That is what I am.

Little Birds are teaching
   Tigresses to smile,
     Innocent of guile:
Smile, I say, not smirkle—
Mouth a semicircle,
     That 's the proper style!

Little Birds are sleeping
   All among the pins,
     Where the loser wins:
Where, I say, he sneezes,
When and how he pleases—
     So the Tale begins.

Little Birds are writing
  Interesting books,
   To be read by cooks:
Read, I say, not roasted—
Letterpress, when toasted,
   Loses its good looks.

Little Birds are playing
  Bagpipes on the shore,
   Where the tourists snore:
'Thanks!' they cry. ''Tis thrilling
Take, oh, take this shilling!
   Let us have no more!'

Little Birds are bathing
  Crocodiles in cream,
   Like a happy dream:
Like, but not so lasting—
Crocodiles, when fasting,
   Are not all they seem!

Little Birds are choking
    Baronets with bun,
      Taught to fire a gun:
Taught, I say, to splinter
Salmon in the winter—
      Merely for the fun.

Little Birds are hiding
    Crimes in carpet-bags,
      Blessed by happy stags:
Blessed, I say, though beaten—
Since our friends are eaten
      When the memory flags.

Little Birds are tasting
    Gratitude and gold,
      Pale with sudden cold:
Pale, I say, and wrinkled—
When the bells have tinkled,
      And the Tale is told.

(1893.)

NONSENSE SONGS

By EDWARD LEAR

THE OWL AND THE PUSSY-CAT

I

The Owl and the Pussy-Cat went to sea
  In a beautiful pea-green boat,
They took some honey, and plenty of money,
  Wrapped up in a five-pound note.
The Owl looked up to the stars above,
  And sang to a small guitar,
'O lovely Pussy! O Pussy, my love,
  What a beautiful Pussy you are,
      You are,
      You are!
What a beautiful Pussy you are!'

75

II

Pussy said to the Owl, 'You elegant fowl!
    How charmingly sweet you sing!
O let us be married! too long we have tarried,
    But what shall we do for a ring?'
They sailed away for a year and a day,
    To the land where the Bong-tree grows,
And there in a wood a Piggy-wig stood,
    With a ring at the end of his nose,
        His nose,
        His nose,
    With a ring at the end of his nose.

III

'Dear Pig, are you willing to sell for one shilling
    Your ring?'   Said the Piggy, 'I will.'
So they took it away, and were married next day
    By the Turkey who lives on the hill.
They dinèd on mince, and slices of quince,
    Which they ate with a runcible spoon;

And hand in hand, on the edge of the sand,
   They danced by the light of the moon,
       The moon,
       The moon,
   They danced by the light of the moon.

                     (1871.)

THE JUMBLIES

I

They went to sea in a Sieve, they did,
   In a Sieve they went to sea:
In spite of all their friends could say,
On a winter's morn, on a stormy day,
   In a Sieve they went to sea!
And when the Sieve turned round and round,
And everyone cried 'You 'll all be drowned!'
They called aloud: 'Our Sieve ain't big,
But we don't care a button! we don't care a fig!
   In a Sieve we 'll go to sea!'
     Far and few, far and few,
       Are the lands where the Jumblies live;
       Their heads are green, and their hands are blue,
        And they went to sea in a Sieve.

II

They sailed away in a Sieve, they did,
  In a Sieve they sailed so fast,
With only a beautiful pea-green veil
Tied with a riband by way of a sail,
  To a small tobacco-pipe mast;
And everyone said, who saw them go,
'O won't they be soon upset, you know!
For the sky is dark, and the voyage is long,
And happen what may, it 's extremely wrong
  In a Sieve to sail so fast!'
    Far and few, far and few,
      Are the lands where the Jumblies live;
      Their heads are green, and their hands are blue,
      And they went to sea in a Sieve.

III

The water it soon came in, it did,
  The water it soon came in;
So to keep them dry, they wrapped their feet
In a pinky paper all folded neat,
  And they fastened it down with a pin.
And they passed the night in a crockery-jar,
And each of them said: 'How wise we are!
Though the sky be dark, and the voyage be long,
Yet we never can think we were rash or wrong,
  While round in our Sieve we spin!'
    Far and few, far and few,
      Are the lands where the Jumblies live;
      Their heads are green, and their hands are blue,
      And they went to sea in a Sieve.

IV

And all night long they sailed away;
  And when the sun went down,
They whistled and warbled a moony song
To the echoing sound of a coppery gong,
  In the shade of the mountains brown.
'O Timballo! how happy we are,
When we live in a Sieve and a crockery-jar.
And all night long in the moonlight pale,
We sail away with a pea-green sail,
  In the shade of the mountains brown!'
    Far and few, far and few,
      Are the lands where the Jumblies live;
      Their heads are green, and their hands are blue,
      And they went to sea in a Sieve.

V

They sailed to the Western Sea, they did,
  To a land all covered with trees,
And they bought an Owl, and a useful Cart,
And a pound of Rice, and a Cranberry Tart,
  And a hive of silvery Bees.
And they bought a Pig, and some green Jackdaws,
And a lovely Monkey with lollipop paws,
And forty bottles of Ring-Bo-Ree,
  And no end of Stilton Cheese.
    Far and few, far and few,
      Are the lands where the Jumblies live;
      Their heads are green, and their hands are blue,
      And they went to sea in a Sieve.

VI

And in twenty years they all came back,
  In twenty years or more,
And everyone said: 'How tall they 've grown!
For they 've been to the Lakes, and the Terrible
    Zone,
  And the hills of the Chankly Bore';
And they drank their health, and gave them a feast
Of dumplings made of beautiful yeast;
And everyone said: 'If we only live,
We too will go to sea in a Sieve—
  To the hills of the Chankly Bore!'
    Far and few, far and few,
      Are the lands where the Jumblies live;
      Their heads are green, and their hands are blue,
      And they went to sea in a Sieve.

          (1871.)

THE NUTCRACKERS AND THE
SUGAR-TONGS

I

The Nutcrackers sate by a plate on the table,
  The Sugar-tongs sate by a plate at his side;
And the Nutcrackers said: 'Don't you wish we were able
  Along the blue hills and green meadows to ride?
Must we drag on this stupid existence for ever,
  So idle and weary so full of remorse—
While everyone else takes his pleasure and never
  Seems happy unless he is riding a horse?

II

'Don't you think we could ride without being instructed?
  Without any saddle, or bridle, or spur?
Our legs are so long, and so aptly constructed,
  I 'm sure that an accident could not occur.
Let us all of a sudden hop down from the table,
  And hustle downstairs, and each jump on a horse!
Shall we try? Shall we go? Do you think we are able?'
  The Sugar-tongs answered distinctly: 'Of course!'

III

So down the long staircase they hopped in a minute,
    The Sugar-tongs snapped, and the Crackers said 'Crack!'
The stable was open, the horses were in it;
    Each took out a pony, and jumped on his back.
The Cat in a fright scrambled out of the doorway,
    The Mice tumbled out of a bundle of hay,
The brown and white Rats, and the black ones from Norway,
    Screamed out: 'They are taking the horses away!'

IV

The whole of the household was filled with amazement,
    The Cups and the Saucers danced madly about,
The Plates and the Dishes looked out of the casement,
    The Saltcellar stood on his head with a shout,
The Spoons with a clatter looked out of the lattice,
    The Mustard-pot climbed up the Gooseberry Pies,
The Soup-ladle peeped through a heap of Veal Patties,
    And squeaked with a ladle-like scream of surprise.

V

The Frying-pan said: 'It 's an awful delusion!'
    The Tea-kettle hissed and grew black in the face;
And they all rushed downstairs in the wildest confusion,
    To see the great Nutcracker-Sugar-tong race.
And out of the stable, with screamings and laughter
    (Their ponies were cream-coloured, speckled with brown,)
The Nutcrackers first, and the Sugar-tongs after,
    Rode all round the yard, and then all round the town.

VI

They rode through the street, and they rode by the station,
    They galloped away to the beautiful shore;
In silence they rode, and 'made no observation,'
    Save this: 'We will never go back any more!'
And still you might hear, till they rode out of hearing,
    The Sugar-tongs snap, and the Crackers say 'Crack!'
Till far in the distance, their forms disappearing,
    They faded away—and they never came back!

(1871.)

CALICO PIE

I

Calico Pie,
The little Birds fly
Down to the calico tree,
Their wings were blue,
And they sang 'Tilly-loo!'
Till away they flew—
And they never came back to me!
They never came back!
They never came back!
They never came back to me!

II

Calico Jam,
The little Fish swam
Over the syllabub sea,
He took off his hat,
To the Sole and the Sprat,
And the Willeby-wat—

But he never came back to me!
He never came back!
He never came back!
He never came back to me!

III

Calico Ban,
The little Mice ran,
To be ready in time for tea,
Flippity flup,
They drank it all up,
And danced in the cup—
But they never came back to me!

They never came back!
They never came back!
They never came back to me!

IV

Calico Drum,
The Grasshoppers come,
The Butterfly, Beetle, and Bee,
Over the ground,
Around and round,
With a hop and a bound—

But they never came back!
They never came back!
They never came back!
They never came back to me!

(1871.)

THE COURTSHIP OF THE YONGHY-BONGHY-BÒ

I

On the Coast of Coromandel
　Where the early pumpkins blow,
　　In the middle of the woods
　Lived the Yonghy-Bonghy-Bò.
Two old chairs, and half a candle—
One old jug without a handle—
　　These were all his worldly goods:
　　In the middle of the woods,
　　These were all the worldly goods,
　Of the Yonghy-Bonghy-Bò,
　Of the Yonghy-Bonghy-Bò.

II

Once, among the Bong-trees walking
  Where the early pumpkins blow,
    To a little heap of stones
    Came the Yonghy-Bonghy-Bò.
There he heard a Lady talking,
To some milk-white Hens of Dorking—
    ''Tis the Lady Jingly Jones!
    On that little heap of stones
    Sits the Lady Jingly Jones!'
  Said the Yonghy-Bonghy-Bò,
  Said the Yonghy-Bonghy-Bò.

III

'Lady Jingly!   Lady Jingly!
  Sitting where the pumpkins blow,
    Will you come and be my wife?'
  Said the Yonghy-Bonghy-Bò.
'I am tired of living singly—
On this coast so wild and shingly—
    I 'm a-weary of my life;
    If you 'll come and be my wife,
    Quite serene would be my life!'—
  Said the Yonghy-Bonghy-Bò,
  Said the Yonghy-Bonghy-Bò.

IV

'On this Coast of Coromandel,
  Shrimps and watercresses grow,
    Prawns are plentiful and cheap,'
  Said the Yonghy-Bonghy-Bò.

'You shall have my chairs and candle,
And my jug without a handle!—
    Gaze upon the rolling deep
    (Fish is plentiful and cheap);
    As the sea, my love is deep!'
Said the Yonghy-Bonghy-Bò,
Said the Yonghy-Bonghy-Bò.

V

Lady Jingly answered sadly,
    And her tears began to flow—
    Your proposal comes too late,
    Mr Yonghy-Bonghy-Bò!
I would be your wife most gladly!'
(Here she twirled her fingers madly)
    'But in England I 've a mate!
    Yes! you 've asked me far too late,
    For in England I 've a mate,
    Mr Yonghy-Bonghy-Bò!
    Mr Yonghy-Bonghy-Bò!

VI

'Mr Jones—(his name is Handel—
    Handel Jones, Esquire, & Co.)
    Dorking fowls delights to send,
    Mr Yonghy-Bonghy-Bò!
Keep, oh! keep your chairs and candle,
And your jug without a handle—
    I can merely be your friend!
    —Should my Jones more Dorkings send,
    I will give you three, my friend!
    Mr Yonghy-Bonghy-Bò!
    Mr Yonghy-Bonghy-Bò!

VII

'Though you 've such a tiny body,
  And your head so large doth grow—
    Though your hat may blow away,
  Mr Yonghy-Bonghy-Bò!
Though you 're such a Hoddy Doddy—
Yet I wish that I could modi-
    fy the words I needs must say!
    Will you please to go away?
    That is all I have to say—
  Mr Yonghy-Bonghy-Bò!
  Mr Yonghy-Bonghy-Bò!'

VIII

Down the slippery slopes of Myrtle,
  Where the early pumpkins blow,
    To the calm and silent sea
  Fled the Yonghy-Bonghy-Bò.
There, beyond the Bay of Gurtle,
Lay a large and lively Turtle—

'You 're the Cove,' he said, 'for me;
On your back beyond the sea,
Turtle, you shall carry me!'
Said the Yonghy-Bonghy-Bò,
Said the Yonghy-Bonghy-Bò.

IX

Through the silent-roaring ocean
Did the Turtle swiftly go;
Holding fast upon his shell
Rode the Yonghy-Bonghy-Bò.
With a sad primeval motion
Towards the sunset isles of Boshen
Still the Turtle bore him well.
Holding fast upon his shell,
'Lady Jingly Jones, farewell!'
Sang the Yonghy-Bonghy-Bò,
Sang the Yonghy-Bonghy-Bò.

X

From the Coast of Coromandel,
Did that Lady never go;
On the heap of stones she mourns
For the Yonghy-Bonghy-Bò.
On the Coast of Coromandel,
In his jug without a handle,
Still she weeps, and daily moans,
On that little heap of stones
To her Dorking Hens she moans,
For the Yonghy-Bonghy-Bò,
For the Yonghy-Bonghy-Bò.

(1877.)

THE POBBLE WHO HAS NO TOES

I

The Pobble who has no toes
    Had once as many as we;
When they said 'Some day you may lose them all'—
    He replied: 'Fish fiddle de-dee!'
And his Aunt Jobiska made him drink,
Lavender water tinged with pink,
For she said: 'The World in general knows
There 's nothing so good for a Pobble's toes!'

II

The Pobble who has no toes,
    Swam across the Bristol Channel;
But before he set out he wrapped his nose
    In a piece of scarlet flannel.
For his Aunt Jobiska said: 'No harm
Can come to his toes if his nose is warm;
And it 's perfectly known that a Pobble's toes
Are safe—provided he minds his nose.'

III

The Pobble swam fast and well,
   And when boats or ships came near him
He tinkledy-binkledy-winkled a bell,
   So that all the world could hear him.
And all the Sailors and Admirals cried,
When they saw him nearing the farther side—
'He has gone to fish, for his Aunt Jobiska's
Runcible Cat with crimson whiskers!'

IV

But before he touched the shore,
   The shore of the Bristol Channel,
A sea-green Porpoise carried away
   His wrapper of scarlet flannel.
And when he came to observe his feet,
Formerly garnished with toes so neat,
His face at once became forlorn
On perceiving that all his toes were gone!

V

And nobody ever knew
   From that dark day to the present,
Whoso had taken the Pobble's toes,
   In a manner so far from pleasant.
Whether the shrimps or crawfish gray,
Or crafty Mermaids stole them away—
Nobody knew; and nobody knows
How the Pobble was robbed of his twice five toes!

VI

The Pobble who has no toes
   Was placed in a friendly Bark,
And they rowed him back, and carried him up,
   To his Aunt Jobiska's Park.
And she made him a feast at his earnest wish
Of eggs and buttercups fried with fish—
And she said: 'It 's a fact the whole world knows,
That Pobbles are happier without their toes.'

(1877.)

THE NEW VESTMENTS

There lived an old man in the Kingdom of Tess,
Who invented a purely original dress;
And when it was perfectly made and complete,
He opened the door, and walked into the street.

By way of a hat he 'd a loaf of Brown Bread,
In the middle of which he inserted his head—
His Shirt was made up of no end of dead Mice,
The warmth of whose skins was quite fluffy and nice—
His Drawers were of Rabbit-skins—so were his Shoes—
His Stockings were skins—but it is not known whose—
His Waistcoat and Trousers were made of Pork Chops—
His Buttons were Jujubes, and Chocolate Drops—
His Coat was all Pancakes with Jam for a border,
And a girdle of Biscuits to keep it in order;
And he wore over all, as a screen from bad weather,
A Cloak of green Cabbage-leaves stitched all together.

He had walked a short way, when he heard a great noise,
Of all sorts of Beasticles, Birdlings, and Boys—
And from every long street and dark lane in the town
Beasts, Birdles, and Boys in a tumult rushed down.
Two Cows and a Calf ate his Cabbage-leaf Cloak—
Four Apes seized his Girdle, which vanished like smoke—
Three Kids ate up half of his Pancaky Coat—
And the tails were devoured by an ancient He Goat—
An army of Dogs in a twinkling tore *up* his
Pork Waistcoat and Trousers to give to their Puppies—
And while they were growling, and mumbling the Chops,
Ten Boys prigged the Jujubes and Chocolate Drops.

He tried to run back to his house, but in vain,
For scores of fat Pigs came again and again—
They rushed out of stables and hovels and doors—
They tore off his stockings, his shoes, and his drawers—
And now from the housetops with screechings descend,
Striped, spotted, white, black, and grey cats without end,
They jumped on his shoulders and knocked off his hat—
When Crows, Ducks, and Hens made a mincemeat of that—
They speedily flew at his sleeves in a trice,
And utterly tore up his Shirt of dead Mice—
They swallowed the last of his Shirt with a squall—
Whereon he ran home with no clothes on at all.

And he said to himself as he bolted the door,
'I will not wear a similar dress any more,
'Any more, any more, any more, never more!'

(1877.)

THE QUANGLE-WANGLE'S HAT

I

On the top of the Crumpetty Tree
    The Quangle-Wangle sat.
But his face you could not see,
    On account of his Beaver Hat.
For his Hat was a hundred and two feet wide,
With ribbons and bibbons on every side
And bells, and buttons, and loops, and lace,
So that nobody ever could see the face
    Of the Quangle-Wangle Quee.

II

The Quangle-Wangle said
    To himself on the Crumpetty Tree:
'Jam; and jelly; and bread;
    Are the best of food for me!

But the longer I live on this Crumpetty Tree,
The plainer than ever it seems to me
That very few people come this way,
And that life on the whole is far from gay!'
    Said the Quangle-Wangle Quee.

III

But there came to the Crumpetty Tree,
  Mr and Mrs Canary;
And they said: 'Did ever you see
  Any spot so charmingly airy?
May we build a nest on your lovely Hat?
Mr Quangle-Wangle, grant us that!
O please let us come and build a nest
Of whatever material suits you best,
    Mr Quangle-Wangle Quee!'

IV

And besides, to the Crumpetty Tree
  Came the Stork, the Duck, and the Owl;
The Snail and the Bumble-Bee,
  The Frog, and the Fimble Fowl;
(The Fimble Fowl, with a Corkscrew leg);
And all of them said: 'We humbly beg,
We may build our homes on your lovely Hat—
Mr Quangle-Wangle, grant us that!
    Mr Quangle-Wangle Quee!'

V

And the Golden Grouse came there,
  And the Pobble who has no toes,
And the small Olympian bear,
  And the Dong with a luminous nose.

And the Blue Baboon, who played the flute,
And the Orient Calf from the Land of Tute,
And the Attery Squash, and the Bisky Bat,
All came and built on the lovely Hat
    Of the Quangle-Wangle Quee.

VI

And the Quangle-Wangle said
    To himself on the Crumpetty Tree:
'When all these creatures move
    What a wonderful noise there 'll be!'
And at night by the light of the Mulberry moon
They danced to the Flute of the Blue Baboon,
On the broad green leaves of the Crumpetty Tree,
And all were as happy as happy could be,
    With the Quangle-Wangle Quee.

(1877.)

LETTERS FROM WONDERLAND, AND OTHER PIECES

By LEWIS CARROLL

I

My one pupil has begun his work with me, and I will give you a description how the lecture is conducted. It is the most important point, you know, that the tutor should be *dignified* and at a distance from the pupil, and that the pupil should be as much as possible *degraded*.

Otherwise, you know, they are not humble enough.

So I sit at the farther end of the room; outside the door (*which is shut*) sits the scout; outside the outer door (*also shut*) sits the sub-scout; half-way downstairs sits the sub-sub-scout; and down in the yard sits the *pupil*.

The questions are shouted from one to the other, and the answers come back in the same way—it is rather confusing until you are well used to it. The lecture goes on something like this:

Tutor. What is twice three?
Scout. What's a rice-tree?
Sub-Scout. When is ice free?
Sub-sub-Scout. What's a nice fee?
Pupil (timidly). Half a guinea!

Sub-sub-Scout. Can't forge any!

Sub-Scout. Ho for Jinny!

Scout. Don't be a Ninny!

Tutor (looks offended, but tries another question). Divide a hundred by twelve!

Scout. Provide wonderful bells!

Sub-Scout. Go ride under it yourself!

Sub-sub-Scout. Deride the dunderheaded elf!

Pupil (surprised). Who do you mean?

Sub-sub-Scout. Doings between!

Sub-Scout. Blue is the screen!

Scout. Soup-tureen.

And so the lecture proceeds.

(1855.)

II

It's been so frightfully hot here that I've been too weak to hold a pen, and even if I had been able, there was no ink—it had all evaporated into a cloud of black steam, and in that state it has been floating about the room, inking the walls and ceiling till they're hardly fit to be seen: to-day it is cooler, and a little has come back into the ink-bottle in the form of black snow.

This hot weather makes me very sad and sulky: I can hardly keep my temper sometimes. For instance, just now the Bishop of Oxford came to see me—it was a civil thing to do, and he meant no harm, poor man: but I was so provoked at his coming in that I threw a book at his head, which I am afraid hurt him a good deal.

This isn't quite true—so you needn't believe it. Don't be in such a hurry to believe next time—I'll tell you why: If you set to work to believe everything, you will tire out the muscles of your mind, and then you 'll be so weak you won't be able to believe the simplest true things. Only last week a friend of mine set to work to believe Jack-the-giant-killer. He managed to do it, but he was so exhausted by it that when I told him it was raining (which was true) he *couldn't* believe it, but rushed out into the street without his hat or umbrella, the consequence of which was his hair got seriously damp, and one curl didn't recover its right shape for nearly two days.

(1864.)

III

Once upon a time there was a little girl, and she had a cross old Uncle—and this little girl had promised to copy out for him a sonnet Mr Rossetti had written about Shakespeare. Well, she didn't do it, you know; and the poor old Uncle's nose kept getting longer and longer, and his temper getting shorter and shorter, and post after post went by, and no sonnet came—— I leave off here to explain how they sent letters in those days: there were no gates, so the gate-posts weren't obliged to stay in one place—consequence of which, they went wandering all over the country—consequence of which, if you wanted to send a letter anywhere, all you had to do was to fasten it to a gate-post that was going in the proper direction (only they sometimes changed their minds, which was awkward). This was called 'sending a letter by the post.' They did things very simply in those days: if you had a lot of money you just dug a hole under the hedge and popped it in: then you said you had 'put it in the bank,' and you felt quite comfortable about it. And the way they travelled was—there were railings the side of the road, and they used to get up, and walk along the top, as steadily as they could, till they tumbled off—which they mostly did very soon.   This was called 'travelling by rail.' —Now to return to the wicked little girl.   The end of her was, that a great black WOLF came, and—I don't like to go on, but nothing was found of her afterwards, except three small bones.

(1864.)

IV

Do not suppose I didn't *write*, hundreds of times: the difficulty has been with the *directing*.   I directed the letters so violently at first, that they went far beyond the mark— some of them were picked up at the other end of Russia. Last week I made a very near shot, and actually succeeded in putting 'Earls Terrace, Kensington,' only I over-did the number, and put 12,000, instead of 12.   If you inquire for the letter at No. 12,000, I dare say they'll give it you. After that, I fell into a feeble state of health, and directed the letters so gently that one of them only reached the other side of the room.   It's lying by the side of the window now.

(1864.)

V

I want to know what you *mean* by calling yourself 'naughty' for not having written sooner!   Naughty, indeed!   Stuff and nonsense!   Do you think *I'd* call myself naughty, if I hadn't written to you, say for fifty years?   Not a bit!   I'd just begin as usual: 'My dear Mary, fifty years ago, you asked me what to do for your kitten, as it had a toothache, and I have just remembered to write about it.   Perhaps the toothache has gone off by this time—if not, wash it carefully

X

nt to explain to you why I did not call yesterday. I was
o miss you, but you see I had so many conversations
way. I tried to explain to the people in the street
was going to see you, but they wouldn't listen; they
ey were in a hurry, which was rude. At last I met a
arrow that I thought would attend to me, but I
't make out what was in it. I saw some features at
en I looked through a telescope and found it was a
nance; then I looked through a microscope and found
a face! I thought it was rather like me, so I fetched
looking-glass to make sure, and then to my great joy
d it was me. We shook hands, and were just begin-
o talk, when myself came up and joined us, and we had
pleasant conversation. I said: 'Do you remember
ve all met at Sandown?' and myself said: 'It was very
ere; there was a child called Magdalen,' and me said:
d to like her a little; not much, you know—only a

(1875.)

XI

will be sorry, and surprised, and puzzled, to hear
queer illness I have had ever since you went. I sent
doctor, and said: 'Give me some medicine, for I'm
He said: 'Nonsense and stuff! You don't want
ne: go to bed!' I said: 'No; it isn't the sort of
ss that wants bed. I'm tired in the *face*.' He
a little grave, and said: 'Oh, it's your *nose* that's
person often talks too much when he thinks he nose
deal.' I said: 'No; it isn't the nose. Perhaps it's

in hasty-pudding, and give it four pin-cushions boiled in
sealing-wax, and just dip the end of its tail in hot coffee.
This remedy has never been known to fail.' There!
That's the proper way to write!

(1866.)

VI

A very curious thing happened to me at half past four
yesterday. Three visitors came knocking at my door,
begging me to let them in. And when I opened the door,
who do you think they were? You'll never guess. Why,
they were three cats! Wasn't it curious? However, they
all looked so cross and disagreeable that I took up the first
thing I could lay my hand on (which happened to be the
rolling-pin) and knocked them all down as flat as pancakes!
'If *you* come knocking at *my* door,' I said, '*I* shall come
knocking at *your* heads.'

Of course I didn't leave them lying flat on the ground like
dried flowers. No, I picked them up, and I was as kind as
I could be to them. I lent them a portfolio for a bed—they
wouldn't have been comfortable in a real bed, you know:
they were too thin—but they were *quite* happy between the
sheets of blotting-paper—and each of them had a pen-wiper
for a pillow. Well, then I went to bed: but first I lent them
the three dinner-bells, to ring if they wanted anything in
the night.

You know I have *three* dinner-bells—the first (which is
the largest) is rung when dinner is *nearly* ready; the second
(which is rather larger) is rung when it is quite ready; and the
third (which is as large as the other two put together) is rung
all the time I am at dinner. Well, I told them they might
ring if they happened to want anything—and, as they rang

all the bells *all* night, I suppose they did want something or other, only I was too sleepy to attend to them.

In the morning I gave them some rat-tail jelly and buttered mice for breakfast, and they were as discontented as they could be. They wanted some boiled pelican, but of course I knew it wouldn't be good for them.

However, I wasn't angry. I gave them a spoonful of ink as a treat: but they were ungrateful for that, and made dreadful faces. But, of course, as it was given them as a treat, they had to drink it. One of them has turned black since: it was a white cat to begin with.

Then I shook hands with them all, and wished them all good-bye, and drove them up the chimney. They seemed very sorry to go, and they took the bells and the portfolio with them. I didn't find this out till after they were gone, and then I was sorry too, and wished for them back again.

What do I mean by 'them'? Never mind.

(*c.* 1866.)

VII

This is indeed dreadful. You have no idea of the grief I am in while I write. I am obliged to use an umbrella to keep the tears from running down on to the paper. Did you come yesterday to be photographed? And were you very angry? Why was I not there? Well, the fact was this—I went for a walk with Bibkins, my dear friend Bibkins—we went many miles from Oxford—fifty—a hundred say. As we were passing a field of sheep a thought crossed my mind, and I said solemnly: 'Dobkins, what o'clock is it?' 'Three,' said Fizkins, surprised at my manner. Tears ran down my cheeks. 'It is the *hour*,' I said. 'Tell me, tell me, Hopkins, what day is it?' 'Why, Monday, of course,' said Lupkins. 'Then it is the *day*!' I groaned, I

wept, I screamed. The sheep rubbed their affectionate noses ag I said, 'you are my oldest frien Nupkins, what year is it?' 'We Pipkins. 'Then it is the *year*.' Tapkins fainted. It was all over cart (attended by the faithful Wo

When I have recovered a little been to the seaside for a few mont another day for photographing. myself, so Zupkins is writing it fo

VIII

I intend to divide my time betw and week about—both are nice, being full of foxes and Peru of l the former place live entirely or butter, you know) and those of the lilies in their hair.

IX

I *never* dance, unless I am all *peculiar way*. There is no use tr to be seen to be believed. The l floor broke through. But then it the beams were only six inches th beams at all: stone arches are muc dancing, *of my peculiar kind*, is to see the rhinoceros, and the hippop Gardens, trying to dance a minuet ing sight.

the *hair*.' Then he looked rather grave, and said: '*Now* I understand: you 've been playing too many hairs on the pianoforte.' 'No, indeed I haven't,' I said, 'and it isn't exactly the *hair*: it 's more about the nose and chin.' Then he looked a good deal graver, and said: 'Have you been walking on your chin lately?' I said: 'No.' 'Well!' he said, 'it puzzles me very much. Do you think that it 's the lips?' 'Of course!' I said. 'That 's exactly what it is!' Then he looked very grave indeed, and said: 'I think you must have been giving too many kisses.' 'Well,' I said, 'I did give *one* kiss to a baby child, a little friend of mine.' 'Think again,' he said; 'are you sure it was only *one*?' I thought again, and said: 'Perhaps it was eleven times.' Then the doctor said: 'You must not give her *any* more till your lips are quite rested again.' 'But what am I to do?' I said. 'Because, you see, I owe her a hundred and eighty-two more.' Then he looked so grave that the tears ran down his cheeks, and he said: 'You may send them to her in a box.'

So I have packed them all very carefully. Tell me if they come safe, or if any are lost on the way.

(1876.)

XII

I came to your door to wish you many happy returns of the day, but the cat met me and took me for a mouse, and hunted me up and down until I could hardly stand. However, somehow I got into the house, and there a mouse met me and took me for a cat, and pelted me with fire-irons, crockery, and bottles. Of course I ran into the street again, and a horse met me and took me for a cart, and dragged me all the way to the station, and the worst of all was when a

cart met me and took me for a horse.   I was harnessed to it
and had to draw it for miles and miles, all the way to
Merrow.   So you see I couldn't get to the room where you
were.

(c. 1876.)

XIII

I like, *very* much indeed, a little mustard with a bit of
beef spread thinly under it; and I like brown sugar—only it
should have some apple pudding mixed with it to keep it
from being too sweet; but perhaps what I like best of all is
salt, with some soup poured over it.   The use of the soup
is to keep the salt from being too dry; and it helps to melt it.
Then there are other things I like; for instance, pins—only
they should always have a cushion put round them to keep
them warm.   And I like two or three handfuls of hair; only
they should always have a little girl's head beneath them to
grow on, or else whenever you open the door they get blown
all over the room, and then they get lost, you know.

(1878.)

XIV

What a lazy thing you must think me, to be so long in
sending you the photograph!   But really I have been
awfully busy, and I 've had to write heaps of letters—wheel-
barrows full, almost.   And it tires me so that generally I
go to bed again a minute after I get up: and sometimes I go
to bed again a minute *before* I get up!   Did you ever hear
of anyone being so tired as that?

(1879.)

XV

Sometimes I get *that* confused, I hardly know which is me and which is the inkstand. The confusion in one's mind doesn't so much matter—but when it comes to putting bread and butter, and orange marmalade, into the *inkstand*; and then dipping pens into *oneself*, and filling *oneself* up with ink, you know, it 's horrid!

(1881.)

XVI

Do you know, I didn't even know of your *existence*? And it was *such* a surprise to hear that you had sent me your love! I felt just as if Nobody had suddenly run into the room, and given me a kiss!

In *some* ways, you know, people that *don't* exist, are much nicer than people that *do*. For instance, people that *don't* exist are never *cross*: and they never *contradict* you: and *they never tread on your toes*! Oh, they 're ever so much nicer than people that *do* exist! However, never mind; you can't help existing, you know; and I dare say you 're *just* as nice as if you didn't.

Please give my love to yourself: don't forget the *kiss* to yourself, please: on the forehead is the best place.

(1891.)

XVII

What do you usually drink at dinner? My lady-guests mostly prefer draught-lemonade—but you can have any of the following beverages:

(1) bottled lemonade; (2) ginger-beer; (3) beer; (4) water; (5) milk; (6) vinegar; (7) ink.

Nobody has yet chosen either No. 6 or No. 7.

(1896.)

XVIII

(*a*) In proceeding to the dining-room, the gentleman gives one arm to the lady he escorts—it is unusual to offer both.

(*b*) To use a fork with your soup, intimating at the same time to your hostess that you are reserving the spoon for the beef steaks, is a practice wholly exploded.

(*c*) On the meat being placed before you, there is no possible objection to your eating it, if so disposed; still in all such delicate cases, be guided entirely by the conduct of those around you.

(*d*) We do not recommend the practice of eating cheese with a knife and fork in one hand and a spoon and wineglass in the other; there is a kind of awkwardness in the action which no amount of practice can entirely dispel.

(1855.)

XIX

It would fare but ill with many of us if we were left to superintend our own digestion and circulation. 'Bless me!' one would cry, 'I forgot to wind up my heart this morning! To think that it has been standing still for the last three hours!'

'I can't walk with you this afternoon,' a friend would say, 'as I have no less than eleven dinners to digest!'

(1884.)

XX

I have always maintained the principle that it is a good rule to take some food—occasionally. The great advantage

of dinner-parties is that it helps you to *see* your friends.   If
you want to *see* a man, offer him something to eat.   It's
the same rule with a mouse.

(1893.)

XXI

'Our Second Experiment,' the Professor announced, 'is
the production of Black Light!   You have seen White
Light, Red Light, Green Light, and so on: but never, till
this wonderful day, have any eyes but mine seen *Black*

Light!   This box,' carefully lifting it upon the table, and
covering it with a heap of blankets, 'is quite full of it.   The
way I made it was this—I took a lighted candle into a dark
cupboard and shut the door.   Of course the cupboard was
then full of *Yellow* Light.   Then I took a bottle of Black

ink, and poured it over the candle: and, to my delight, every atom of the Yellow Light turned *Black*! Then I filled a box with it. And now—would anyone like to get under the blankets and see it?'

Bruno crawled under the blankets, and after a minute or two crawled out again.

'What did you see in the box?' Sylvie eagerly inquired.

'I saw *nothing*!' Bruno sadly replied. 'It were too dark!'

'He has described the appearance of the thing exactly!' the Professor exclaimed with enthusiasm. 'Black Light, and Nothing, look so extremely alike, at first sight, that I don't wonder he failed to distinguish them!'

(1893.)

XXII

'You must explain to me, please,' the Professor said with an anxious look, '*which* is the Lion, and *which* is the Gardener. It's *most* important not to get two such animals confused together. And one's very liable to do it in their case—both having mouths, you know.

'Now, for instance, there's the rabbit hutch and the hall clock. One gets a little confused with *them*—both having doors, you know. Now, only yesterday—would you believe it?—I put some lettuces into the clock, and tried to wind up the rabbit!'

'Did the rabbit *go*, after you wound it up?' said Bruno.

'Go? I should think it *did* go! And wherever it's gone to—that's what I can't find out!'

(1889.)

XXIII

'It *was* proud of its tail! You never saw a Crocodile so proud! Why, it could go round and walk on the top of its tail, and along its back; I watched it, and it walked on tip-toe, so as it wouldn't wake itself, 'cause it thought it was

asleep. And it got both its paws on its tail. And it walked and it walked all the way along its back, all the way to its head. And it walked and it walked on its forehead. And it walked a tiny little way down its nose!'

(1889.)

XXIV

Once there were a Mouse and a Crocodile and a Man and a Goat and a Lion. And the Mouse found a shoe, and it thought it was a mouse-trap. So it got right in, and it stayed in ever so long—'cause it thought it couldn't get out again. It was a clever mouse—it knew it couldn't get out of traps.

It jumped and it jumped, and at last it got right out again. And it looked at the mark in the shoe, and the Man's name was in it. So it knew it wasn't its own shoe.

So the Mouse gave the Man his shoe. And the Man

was very glad, 'cause he hadn't got but one shoe, and he was hopping to get the other.   And the Man took the Goat out of the sack.   And he said to the Goat: 'You will walk about here till I come back.'   And he went and he tumbled into a deep hole.   And the Goat walked round and round.

And it walked under the tree.   And it wagged its tail. And it looked up in the tree, and it sang a sad little song.

And when it had sung all the song, it ran away—to get along to look for the Man, you know.   And the Crocodile got along after it, to bite it.   And the Mouse got along after the Crocodile.   The Crocodile wasn't running, and he wasn't crawling: he went struggling along like a portmanteau.   And he held his chin ever so high in the air—'cause he hadn't got a toothache.   And of course he had blankets: do you think crocodiles go walks without blankets? And he frowned with his eyebrows, and the Goat was very frightened at his eyebrows—and I should think you would, if they 'd got a crocodile fastened to them, like these had!

And so the Man jumped, and he jumped, and at last he got right out of the hole. And he ran away to look for the Goat. And he heard the Lion grunting, and its mouth was like a large cupboard—it had plenty of room in its mouth. And the Lion ran after the Man, to eat him. And the Mouse ran after the Lion.

And first he caught the Crocodile, and then he didn't catch the Lion. And when he 'd caught the Crocodile, he wrenched out the tooth it was going to bite the Goat with.

Then the Lion sprang at the Man. But it came so slowly, it was three weeks in the air, and the Man didn't wait for all that time; he sold his house, and he packed up his things, while the Lion was coming. And he went and he lived in another town.

So the Lion ate the wrong man.

(1889.)

XXV

STANZA OF ANGLO-SAXON POETRY

Twas bryllyg, and the slythy toves
Did gyre and gymble in the wabe:
All mimsy were the borogoves:
And the mome raths outgrabe.

The meanings of the words are as follows:

Bryllyg (derived from the verb *to bryl* or *broil*): 'The time of broiling dinner, i.e. the close of the afternoon.'

Slythy (compounded of *slimy* and *lithe*): 'Smooth and active.'

Tove: A species of badger. They had smooth white hair, long hind legs, and short horns like a stag; lived chiefly on cheese.

Gyre, verb (derived from *gyaour* or *giaour*, 'a dog'): 'To scratch like a dog.'

Gymble (whence *gimblet*): 'To screw out holes in anything.'

Wabe (derived from the verb *to swab* or *soak*): 'The side of a hill' (from its being *soaked* by the rain).

Mimsy (whence *mimserable* and *miserable*): 'Unhappy.'

Borogove: An extinct kind of parrot. They had no wings, beaks turned up, and made their nests under sundials: lived on veal.

Mome (hence *solemome, solemone* and *solemn*): 'Grave.'

Rath: A species of land turtle. Head erect: mouth like a shark: forelegs curved out so that the animal walked on its knees: smooth green body: lived on swallows and oysters.

Outgrabe, past tense of the verb *to outgribe* (it is connected with old verb *to grike* or *shrike*, from which are derived 'shriek' and 'creak'): 'Squeaked.'

Hence the literal English of the passage is: 'It was evening, and the smooth active badgers were scratching and boring holes in the hillside; all unhappy were the parrots; and the grave turtles squeaked out.'

There were probably sundials on the top of the hill, and

the 'borogoves' were afraid that their nests would be under-mined.   The hill was probably full of the nests of 'raths,' which ran out, squeaking with fear, on hearing the 'toves' scratching outside.   This is an obscure, but yet deeply affecting, relic of ancient poetry.

(1855.)

EIGHT-AND-FORTY
NONSENSE LIMERICKS

By EDWARD LEAR

There was an Old Man with a beard,
Who said: 'It is just as I feared!—
    Two Owls and a Hen,
    Four Larks and a Wren,
Have all built their nests in my beard!'

There was an Old Man with a nose,
Who said: 'If you choose to suppose
   That my nose is too long,
   You are certainly wrong!'
That remarkable man with a nose.

There was a Young Lady whose chin
Resembled the point of a pin;
   So she had it made sharp,
   And purchased a harp,
And played several tunes with her chin.

There was an Old Lady of Chertsey,
Who made a remarkable curtsey;
    She twirled round and round
    Till she sank underground,
Which distressed all the people of Chertsey.

There was an Old Man of Madras,
Who rode on a cream-coloured ass;
    But the length of its ears
    So promoted his fears,
That it killed that Old Man of Madras.

There was an Old Man who supposed
That the street door was partially closed;
But some very large rats
Ate his coats and his hats,
While that futile Old Gentleman dozed.

There was an Old Man of Nepaul,
From his horse had a terrible fall;
But, though split quite in two,
With some very strong glue
They mended that Man of Nepaul.

There was an Old Person whose habits
Induced him to feed upon rabbits;
   When he 'd eaten eighteen
   He turned perfectly green,
Upon which he relinquished those habits.

There was an Old Man of Peru,
Who watched his wife making a stew:
   But once by mistake,
   In a stove she did bake
That unfortunate Man of Peru.

There was a Young Lady whose nose
Was so long that it reached to her toes;
   So she hired an old lady,
   Whose conduct was steady,
To carry that wonderful nose.

There was an Old Person of Rheims,
Who was troubled with horrible dreams;
   So, to keep him awake,
   They fed him on cake,
Which amused that Old Person of Rheims.

There was an Old Man of the South,
Who had an immoderate mouth;
    But in swallowing a dish,
    That was quite full of fish,
He was choked, that Old Man of the South.

There was an Old Person of Tring,
Who embellished his nose with a ring;
    He gazed at the moon
    Every evening in June,
That ecstatic Old Person of Tring.

There was an Old Man of Coblenz,
The length of whose legs was immense;
    He went with one prance
    From Turkey to France,
That surprising Old Man of Coblenz.

There was an Old Man of Leghorn,
The smallest that ever was born;
    But quickly snapped up he
    Was once by a puppy,
Who devoured that Old Man of Leghorn.

There was an Old Man of The Hague,
Whose ideas were excessively vague;
    He built a balloon
    To examine the moon,
That deluded Old Man of The Hague.

There was an Old Man of the coast,
Who placidly sat on a post;
    But when it was cold
    He relinquished his hold
And called for some hot buttered toast.

There was an Old Man who said: 'Hush!
I perceive a young bird in this bush!'
  When they said 'Is it small?'
  He replied: 'Not at all!
It is four times as big as the bush!'

There was an Old Man of the West,
Who never could get any rest;
  So they set him to spin
  On his nose and his chin,
Which cured that Old Man of the West.

There was an Old Person of Gretna,
Who rushed down the crater of Etna;
   When they said 'Is it hot?'
   He replied: 'No, it 's not!'
That mendacious Old Person of Gretna.

There was an Old Person of Spain,
Who hated all trouble and pain;
   So he sat on a chair,
   With his feet in the air,
That umbrageous Old Person of Spain.

There was an Old Man on whose nose,
Most birds of the air could repose;
    But they all flew away
    At the closing of day,
Which relieved that Old Man and his nose.

There was an Old Man of Aosta,
Who possessed a large cow, but he lost her;
    But they said: 'Don't you see
    She has rushed up a tree?
You invidious Old Man of Aosta!'

There was an Old Person of Ewell,
Who chiefly subsisted on gruel;
  But to make it more nice
  He inserted some mice,
Which refreshed that Old Person of Ewell.

There was an Old Man, who when little
Fell casually into a Kettle;
  But, growing too stout,
  He could never get out,
So he passed all his life in that Kettle.

There was an Old Man of Thermopylae,
Who never did anything properly;
    But they said: 'If you choose
    To boil Eggs in your Shoes,
You shall never remain in Thermopylae.

There was an Old Person of Pinner,
As thin as a lath, if not thinner;
    They dressed him in white,
    And roll'd him up tight,
That elastic Old Person of Pinner.

There was an Old Man who said: 'How
Shall I flee from that horrible cow?
    I will sit on this stile,
    And continue to smile,
Which may soften the heart of that cow.'

There was an Old Man of the Dargle,
Who purchased six barrels of Gargle;
    For he said: 'I 'll sit still,
    And will roll them down hill,
For the fish in the depths of the Dargle.'

There was an Old Person of Slough,
Who danced at the end of a Bough;
But they said: 'If you sneeze,
You might damage the trees,
You imprudent Old Person of Slough.'

There was an Old Person of Ware,
Who rode on the back of a Bear;
When they ask'd 'Does it trot?'
He said: 'Certainly not!
He 's a Moppsikon Floppsikon Bear!'

There was a Young Person of Janina,
Whose uncle was always a-fanning her;
    When he fanned off her head,
    She smiled sweetly and said:
'You propitious Old Person of Janina!'

There was an Old Person of Cassel,
Whose Nose finished off in a Tassel;
    But they call'd out: 'Oh well!—
    Don't it look like a bell!'
Which perplexed that Old Person of Cassel.

There was an Old Man of Cashmere,
Whose movements were scroobious and queer;
    Being slender and tall,
    He looked over a wall,
And perceived two fat Ducks of Cashmere.

There was an Old Man of Spithead,
Who opened the window and said:
    'Fil-jomble, fil-jumble,
    Fil-rumble-come-tumble!'
That doubtful Old Man of Spithead.

There was an Old Person of Wilts,
Who constantly walked upon Stilts;
    He wreathed them with lilies
    And daffy-down-dillies,
That elegant Person of Wilts.

There was an Old Man of Port Grigor,
Whose actions were noted for vigour;
    He stood on his head,
    Till his waistcoat turned red,
That eclectic Old Man of Port Grigor.

There was an Old Man of West Dumpet,
Who possessed a large Nose like a Trumpet;
    When he blew it aloud,
    It astonished the crowd,
And was heard through the whole of West Dumpet.

There was an Old Man of Ancona,
Who found a small Dog with no Owner,
    Which he took up and down
    All the streets of the town;
That anxious Old Man of Ancona.

There was an Old Person of Ickley,
Who could not abide to ride quickly;
    He rode to Karnak
    On a Tortoise's back,
That moony Old Person of Ickley.

There was an Old Person of Bray,
Who sang through the whole of the Day
    To his Ducks and his Pigs,
    Whom he fed upon Figs,
That valuable Person of Bray.

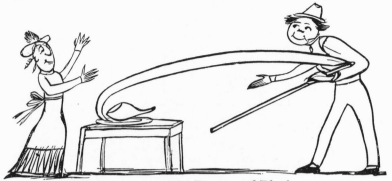

There was an Old Person of Blythe,
Who cut up his Meat with a Scythe;
　　When they said 'Well, I never!'
　　He cried: 'Scythes for ever!'
That lively Old Person of Blythe.

There was an Old Person of Grange,
Whose manners were scroobious and strange;
　　He sailed to St Blubb,
　　In a Waterproof Tub,
That aquatic Old Person of Grange.

There was an Old Person of Rye,
Who went up to town on a Fly;
    But they said: 'If you cough,
    You are safe to fall off!
You abstemious Old Person of Rye!'

There was a Young Lady whose Nose
Continually prospers and grows;
    When it grew out of sight,
    She exclaimed in a fright:
'Oh!   Farewell to the end of my Nose!'

There was a Young Lady of Corsica,
Who purchased a little brown Saucy-cur,
  Which she fed upon Ham
  And hot Raspberry Jam,
That expensive Young Lady of Corsica.

There was a Young Person of Ayr,
Whose Head was remarkably square:
  On the top, in fine weather,
  She wore a Gold Feather,
Which dazzled the people of Ayr.

There was an Old Man of Peru,
Who never knew what he should do;
    So he tore off his hair,
    And behaved like a bear,
That intrinsic Old Man of Peru.

THE ENGLISH STRUWWELPETER

OR

PRETTY STORIES & FUNNY PICTURES

When the children have been good,
That is, be it understood,
Good at meal-times, good at play,
Good all night, and good all day,
They shall have the pretty things
Merry Christmas always brings.
Naughty, romping girls and boys,
Tear their clothes and make a noise,
Spoil their pinafores and frocks,
And deserve no Christmas-box,
Such as these shall never look
At this pretty Picture-Book.

147

1. SHOCK-HEADED PETER

Shock-headed Peter!   There he stands,
With his horrid hair and hands.
See, his nails are never cut;
They are grim'd as black as soot;
And, the sloven, I declare,
He has never comb'd his hair;
Anything to me is sweeter
Than to see Shock-headed Peter.

2. THE STORY OF CRUEL FREDERICK

Here is cruel Frederick, see!
A horrid wicked boy was he;
He caught the flies, poor little things,
And then tore off their tiny wings,
He kill'd the birds, and broke the chairs,
And threw the kitten down the stairs,
And oh! far worse than all beside,
He whipp'd poor Mary, till she cried.

The trough was full, and faithful Tray
Came out to drink one sultry day;
He wagg'd his tail, and wet his lip,
When cruel Fred snatch'd up a whip,
And whipp'd poor Tray till he was sore,
And kick'd and whipp'd him more and more.
At this, good Tray grew very red,
And growl'd and bit him till he bled;

Then you should only have been by,
To see how Fred did scream and cry!

So Frederick had to go to bed;
His leg was very sore and red!

The Doctor came and shook his head
And made a very great to-do,
And gave him nasty physic too.
But good dog Tray is happy now;

He has no time to say 'Bow-wow!'
He seats himself in Frederick's chair
And laughs to see the nice things
    there;
The soup he swallows, sup by sup—
And eats the pies and puddings up.

3. THE DREADFUL STORY ABOUT HARRIET AND THE MATCHES

It almost makes me cry to tell
What foolish Harriet befell.
Mamma and Nurse went out one day
And left her all alone to play;
Now, on the table close at hand,
A box of matches chanc'd to stand;
And kind Mamma and Nurse had told her,
That, if she touch'd them, they should scold her.
But Harriet said: 'Oh, what a pity!
For, when they burn, it is so pretty;
They crackle so, and spit, and flame;
Mamma, too, often does the same.'

    The pussy-cats heard this,
    And they began to hiss,
    And stretch their claws
    And raise their paws;
    'Me-ow,' they said, 'me-ow, me-o,
    You 'll burn to death, if you do so.'

But Harriet would not take advice,
She lit a match, it was so nice!
It crackled so, it burn'd so clear—
Exactly like the picture here.
She jump'd for joy and ran about
And was too pleas'd to put it out.

The pussy-cats saw this
And said: 'Oh, naughty, naughty Miss!'
And stretch'd their claws
And rais'd their paws:
''Tis very, very wrong, you know,
Me-ow, mee-o, me-ow, me-o,
You will be burnt, if you do so.'

And see!   Oh! what a dreadful thing!
The fire has caught her apron-string;
Her apron burns, her arms, her hair;
She burns all over, everywhere.

Then how the pussy-cats did mew,
What else, poor pussies, could they do?
They scream'd for help, 'twas all in vain!
So then they said: 'We 'll scream again;
Make haste, make haste, me-ow, me-o,
She 'll burn to death, we told her so.'

So she was burnt, with all her clothes,
And arms, and hands, and eyes, and nose;

Till she had nothing more to lose
Except her little scarlet shoes;
And nothing else but these was found
Among her ashes on the ground.

And when the good cats sat beside
The smoking ashes, how they cried!
'Me-ow, me-oo, me-ow, me-oo,
What will Mamma and Nursy do?'
Their tears ran down their cheeks so fast;
They made a little pond at last.

4. THE STORY OF THE INKY BOYS

As he had often done before,
The woolly-headed black-a-moor
One nice fine summer's day went out
To see the shops and walk about;
And as he found it hot, poor fellow,
He took with him his green umbrella.
Then Edward, little noisy wag,
Ran out and laugh'd and wav'd his flag;
And William came in jacket trim
And brought his wooden hoop with him;
And Arthur, too, snatch'd up his toys
And join'd the other naughty boys;

So, one and all set up a roar
And laugh'd and hooted more and more,
And kept on singing—only think!—
'Oh! Blacky, you 're as black as ink.'
Now tall Agrippa lived close by—
So tall, he almost touch'd the sky;
He had a mighty inkstand too,
In which a great goose-feather grew;
He call'd out in an angry tone:
'Boys, leave the black-a-moor alone!
For if he tries with all his might,
He cannot change from black to white.'
But ah! they did not mind a bit
What great Agrippa said of it;
But went on laughing as before,
And hooting at the black-a-moor.

Then great Agrippa foams with rage,
Look at him on this very page!
He seizes Arthur, seizes Ned,
Takes William by his little head;

And they may scream and kick and call,
Into the ink he dips them all;
Into the inkstand, one, two, three,
Till they are black, as black can be;

Look up! look up! and you shall see.
Ah! there they are, and there they run!
The black-a-moor enjoys the fun.
They have been made as black as crows,
Quite black all over, eyes and nose,
And legs, and arms, and heads, and toes,
And trousers, pinafores, and toys—
The silly little inky boys!
Because they set up such a roar,
And teas'd the harmless black-a-moor.

5. THE STORY OF THE MAN THAT WENT OUT SHOOTING

This is the man that
  shoots the hares;
This is the coat he
  always wears:
With game-bag,
  powder-horn
    and gun
He's going out
  to have some
    fun.

The hare sits snug
  in leaves and grass,
And laughs to see the green man pass.
He finds it hard, without a pair
Of spectacles, to shoot the hare.

Now, as the sun grew very hot,
And he a heavy gun had got,
He lay down underneath a tree
And went to sleep quite happily.

And, while he slept like any top,
The little hare came, hop, hop, hop,
Took gun and spectacles, and then
On her hind legs went off again.

The green man wakes and sees her place
The spectacles upon her face;
And now she's trying all she can
To shoot the sleepy, green-coat man.

He cries and screams and runs away;
The hare runs after him all day,
And hears him call out everywhere:
'Help! Fire! Help! The hare! The hare!'

At last he stumbled at the well
Head over ears, and in he fell.
The hare stopp'd short, took aim, and hark!
Bang went the gun—she miss'd her mark!

The poor man's wife was drinking up
Her coffee in her coffee-cup;
The gun shot cup and saucer through;
'Oh dear!' cried she, 'what shall I do?'

There liv'd close by the cottage there
The hare's own child, the little hare;
And while she stood upon her toes,
The coffee fell and burn'd her nose.
'Oh dear!' she cried, with spoon in hand,
'Such fun I do not understand.'

6. THE STORY OF LITTLE SUCK-A-THUMB

One day, Mamma said: 'Conrad dear,
I must go out and leave you here.
But mind now, Conrad, what I say,
Don't suck your thumb while I 'm away.
The great tall tailor always comes
To little boys that suck their thumbs,
And ere they dream what he 's about,
He takes his great sharp scissors out
And cuts their thumbs clean off—and then,
You know, they never grow again.'

Mamma had scarcely turn'd
    her back,
The thumb was in, Alack!
    Alack!
The door flew open, in he
    ran,
The great, long, red-legg'd
    scissor-man.
Oh! children, see! the tailor's come
And caught out little Suck-a-Thumb.

Snip! snap! snip! the scissors go;
And Conrad cries out: 'Oh! oh! oh!'
Snip! snap! snip!   They go so fast,
That both his thumbs are off at last.

Mamma comes home; there Conrad
    stands,
And looks quite sad, and shows his
    hands—
'Ah!' said Mamma, 'I knew he 'd
    come
To naughty little Suck-a-Thumb.'

7. THE STORY OF AUGUSTUS WHO WOULD NOT HAVE ANY SOUP

Augustus was a chubby lad;
Fat ruddy cheeks Augustus had;
And everybody saw with joy
The plump and hearty healthy boy.
He ate and drank as he was told,
And never let his soup get cold.
But one day, one cold winter's day,
He scream'd out: 'Take the soup away!
O take the nasty soup away!
I won't have any soup to-day.'

Next day, now look, the picture shows
How lank and lean Augustus grows!
Yet, though he feels so weak and ill,
The naughty fellow cries out still:
'Not any soup for me, I say:
O take the nasty soup away!
I won't have any soup to-day.'

The third day comes; O what
    a sin
To make himself so pale and
    thin!
Yet, when the soup is put on table,
He screams, as loud as he is able:
'Not any soup for me, I say:
O take the nasty soup away!
I won't have any soup to-day.'

Look at him, now the fourth day 's come!
He scarcely weighs a sugar-plum;

He 's like a little bit of
    thread;
And on the fifth day, he
    was—dead!

8. THE STORY OF FIDGETY PHILIP

'Let me see if Philip can
Be a little gentleman;
Let me see if he is able
To sit still for once at table:'
Thus Papa bade Phil behave;
And Mamma look'd very grave.

But fidgety Phil,
He won't sit still;
He wiggles
And giggles,
And then, I declare,
Swings backwards and forwards
And tilts up his chair,
Just like any rocking-horse—
'Philip! I am getting cross!'

See the naughty restless child
Growing still more rude and wild,
Till his chair falls over quite.
Philip screams with all his might,
Catches at the cloth, but then
That makes matters worse again.
Down upon the ground they fall,
Glasses, plates, knives, forks and all.
How Mamma did fret and frown,
When she saw them tumbling down!
And Papa made such a face!
Philip is in sad disgrace.

Where is Philip, where is he?
Fairly cover'd up, you see!
Cloth and all are lying on him;
He has pull'd down all upon him.
What a terrible to-do!
Dishes, glasses, snapt in two!
Here a knife, and there a fork!
Philip, this is cruel work.

Table all so bare, and ah!
Poor Papa and poor Mamma
Look quite cross, and wonder how
They shall make their dinner now.

9. THE STORY OF JOHNNY HEAD-IN-AIR

As he trudg'd along to school,
It was always Johnny's rule
To be looking at the sky
And the clouds that floated by;
But what just before him lay,
In his way,
Johnny never thought about;
So that everyone cried out:
'Look at little Johnny there,
Little Johnny Head-in-Air!'

Running just in Johnny's way,
Came a little dog one day;
Johnny's eyes were still astray
Up on high,
In the sky;
And he never heard them cry:
'Johnny, mind, the dog is nigh!'
Bump!
Dump!
Down they fell, with such a thump,
Dog and Johnny in a lump!

Once, with head as high as ever,
Johnny walk'd beside the river.
Johnny watch'd the swallows trying
Which was cleverest at flying.
Oh! what fun!
Johnny watch'd the bright round sun
Going in and coming out;

This was all he thought about.
So he strode on, only think!
To the river's very brink,
Where the bank was high and steep,
And the water very deep;
And the fishes, in a row,
Stared to see him coming so.

One step more!   Oh! sad to tell!
Headlong in poor Johnny fell.
And the fishes, in dismay,
Wagg'd their tails and ran away.
There lay Johnny on his face,
With his nice red writing-case;
But, as they were passing by,
Two strong men had heard him cry;
And, with sticks, these two strong men
Hook'd poor Johnny out again.

Oh! you should have seen him
     shiver
When they pull'd him from the
     river.
He was in a sorry plight!
Dripping wet, and such a fright!
Wet all over, everywhere,
Clothes, and arms, and face, and hair:
Johnny never will forget
What it is to be so wet.
And the fishes, one, two, three,
Are come back again, you see;
Up they came the moment after,
To enjoy the fun and laughter.

Each popp'd out his little head,
And, to tease poor Johnny, said:
'Silly little Johnny, look,
You have lost your writing-book!'

10. THE STORY OF FLYING ROBERT

When the rain comes tumbling down
In the country or the town,
All good little girls and boys
Stay at home and mind their toys.
Robert thought—'No, when it pours,
It is better out of doors.'
Rain it *did*, and in a minute
Bob was in it.

What a wind!   Oh! how it whistles
Through the trees and flow'rs and thistles!
It has caught his red umbrella;
It has caught him, silly fellow;
Up he flies
To the skies.
No one heard his screams and cries,
Through the clouds the rude wind bore him,
And his hat flew on before him.
Soon they got to such a height,
They were nearly out of sight!
And the hat went up so high,
That it really touch'd the sky.
No one ever yet could tell
Where they stopp'd, or where they fell:
Only, this one thing is plain,
Bob was never seen again!

HALF-A-HUNDRED NURSERY NONSENSE RHYMES

I

Anna Elise, she jumped with surprise;
The surprise was so quick, it played her a trick;
The trick was so rare, she jumped in a chair;
The chair was so frail, she jumped in a pail;
The pail was so wet, she jumped in a net;
The net was so small, she jumped on the ball;
The ball was so round, she jumped on the ground;
And ever since then she 's been turning around.

(1920.)

II

Baby and I
Were baked in a pie,
The gravy was wonderful hot.
We had nothing to pay
To the baker that day
And so we crept out of the pot.

(1843.)

III

How many miles to Babylon?
Three score miles and ten.
Can I get there by candlelight?
Yes, and back again.
If your heels are nimble and tight,
You may get there by candlelight.

(1805.)

IV

Barber, barber, shave a pig,
How many hairs will make a wig?
Four and twenty, that's enough.
Give the barber a pinch of snuff.

(1842.)

V

Barney Bodkin broke his nose,
Without feet we can't have toes;
Crazy folk are always mad,
Want of money makes us sad.
A farthing rushlight's very small,
    Doctors wear large bushy wigs,
One that's dumb can never bawl,
    Pickled pork is made of pigs.

(1812.)

VI

Peter, Peter, pumpkin eater,
Had a wife and couldn't keep her;
He put her in a pumpkin shell,
And there he kept her very well.

(1825.)

VII

Three children sliding on the ice,
　　Upon a summer's day,
As it fell out, they *all* fell in,
　　The rest they ran away.

(1712.)

VIII

As I went to Bonner
　I met a pig
　Without a wig,
Upon my word of honour.

(1830.)

IX

We 're all in the dumps,
　For diamonds are trumps;
The kittens are gone to St Pauls!
　The babies are bit,
　The moon's in a fit,
And houses are built without walls.

(1842.)

X

What are little boys made of?
What are little boys made of?
　Frogs and snails
　And puppy-dogs' tails,
That 's what little boys are made of.

(1844.)

XI

A cat came fiddling out of a barn,
With a pair of bagpipes under her arm;
She could sing nothing but fiddle-cum-fee,
The mouse has married the humble-bee.

(1840.)

XII

Dickery, dickery, dare!
The pig flew up in the air;
The man in brown
Soon brought him down—
Dickery, dickery, dare!

(1844.)

XIII

On Christmas Eve I turned the spit,
I burnt my fingers, I feel it yet;
The cock sparrow flew over the table;
The pot began to play with the ladle.
The ladle stood up like an angry man,
And vowed he 'd fight the frying-pan;
The frying-pan behind the door
Said he never saw the like before—
And the kitchen clock I was going to wind
Said he never saw the like behind.

(1844 and 1908.)

XIV

As I was going to Derby,
Upon a market day,
I met the finest ram, sir,
That ever was fed on hay.

This ram was fat behind, sir,
 This ram was fat before,
This ram was ten yards high, sir,
 Indeed he was no more.

The wool upon his back, sir,
 Reached up unto the sky,
The eagles built their nests there,
 For I heard the young ones cry.

The horns upon this ram, sir,
 They reached up to the Moon;
A man went up in January
 And didn't come down till June.

Indeed, sir, it 's the truth, sir,
 For I never was taught to lie,
And if you go to Derby, sir,
 You may eat a bit of the pie.

      (1827, etc.)

XV

In a cottage in Fife
Lived a man and his wife,
Who, believe me, were comical folk;
 For, to people's surprise,
 They both saw with their eyes,
And their tongues moved whenever they spoke!
 When quite fast asleep,
 I 've been told that to keep
Their eyes open they could not contrive;
 And they walked on their feet,
 And 'twas thought what they eat
Helped, with drinking, to keep them alive!

      (1805.)

XVI

Fiddle-de-dee, fiddle-de-dee,
The fly shall marry the bumble-bee.
They went to the church, and married was she;
The fly has married the bumble-bee.

(1842.)

XVII

Hey diddle diddle,
The cat and the fiddle,
The cow jumped over the Moon;
The little dog laughed
To see such craft,
And the dish ran away with the spoon.

(1765.)

XVIII

I had a little horse,
His name was Dobbin Grey,
His head was made of pea-straw,
His tail was made of hay.
He could amble, he could trot
All around the chimney top,
With a little mustard pot—
High-gee-ho! and clipperty-clop!

(1805.)

XIX

Hoddley, poddley, puddle and fogs,
Cats are to marry the poodle dogs;
Cats in blue jackets and dogs in red hats:
What will become of the mice and rats?

(1932.)

XX

Hokey-pokey, winky, wang,
Slippery-sloppery, buskey bang,
How do you like your 'taties done?
'Boiled in whisky, boiled in rum,'
    Says the King of the Cannibal Islands.

                (1845 and 1949.)

XXI

As I went over the water,
    The water went over me.
I saw two little blackbirds
    Sitting on a tree:
One called me a rascal,
    And one called me a thief;
I took my little black stick
    And knocked out all their teeth.

                (1853.)

XXII

I 'll tell you a story
    About Jack a Nory,
And now my story 's begun;
    I 'll tell you another
    Of Jack and his brother,
And now my story is done.

                (1760.)

XXIII

Jerry Hall
Is so small,
A rat could eat him
Hat and all.

                (1924.)

XXIV

Here am I,
Little Jumping Joan;
When nobody 's with me,
I 'm all alone.

(1808.)

XXV

There was a king, and he had three daughters,
And they all lived in a basin of water;
    The basin bended—
    My story 's ended.
If the basin had been stronger,
My story would have been longer.

(1844.)

XXVI

Ladybird, ladybird,
    Fly away home,
Your house is on fire
    And your children are gone;
All except one
    And that 's little Ann,
And she has crept under
    The warming pan.

(1744 and 1840.)

XXVII

The lion and the unicorn
    Were fighting for the crown,
The lion beat the unicorn
    All round the town.

Some gave them white bread,
And some gave them brown;
Some gave them plum cake
And drummed them out of town.

(1708 and 1805.)

XXVIII

Hey, diddle doubt,
My fire is out,
My little maid's not at home;
So saddle my hog,
And bridle my dog,
And bring my little maid home.

(1784.)

XXIX

There was a man who had no eyes,
He went abroad to view the skies;
He saw a tree with fruit upon it,
Took none off and left none on it.

(1853.)

XXX

The Man in the Moon
Came down too soon,
And asked his way to Norwich;
He went by the south,
And burnt his mouth
With supping cold pease-porridge.

(1784.)

XXXI

The Man in the Moon drinks claret,
With powdered-beef, turnip, and carrot;
   A cup of old Malaga sack
   Will fire his bush at his back.

(1660.)

XXXII

Mary, Mary, quite contrary,
   How does your garden grow?
With silver bells and cockle shells,
   And pretty maids all in a row.

(1744.)

XXXIII

Three blind mice, see how they run!
They all ran after the farmer's wife,
Who cut off their tails with a carving knife;
Did ever you see such a thing in your life
   As three blind mice?

(1609 and 1843.)

XXXIV

Six little mice sat down to spin;
Pussy passed by, and she peeped in.
'What are you doing, my little men?'
'Making coats for gentlemen.'
'Shall I come in and cut off your threads?'
'Oh no, Mistress Pussy, you 'd bite off our heads!'

(1840.)

XXXV

As I was walking along in the fields,
I saw St Paul's Steeple running on wheels.

On top of the Steeple, oh what should I see
But a fine young sapling codling tree.

When the codlings were ripe they began to fall;
They killed six thousand people and all.

A shoulder of mutton jumped over from France,
And the music did play and the people did dance.

(1676 and 1840.)

XXXVI

There was an old woman called nothing at all.
Who lived in a dwelling exceedingly small.
A man stretched his mouth to its utmost extent,
And down at one gulp house and old woman went.

(1843.)

XXXVII

Old Mother Shuttle
Lived in a coal-scuttle
Along with her dog and her cat;
What they ate I can't tell,
But 'tis known very well
That not one of the party was fat.

Old Mother Shuttle
Scoured out her coal-scuttle,
And washed both her dog and her cat;
The cat scratched her nose,
So they came to hard blows,
And who was the gainer by that?

(1805.)

XXXVIII

There was an old woman, her name it was Peg;
Her head was of wood, and she wore a cork leg.
Her neighbours all pitched her into the water,
Her leg was drowned first, and her head followed after.

(1844.)

XXXIX

Little King Pippin he built a fine hall,
Pie-crust and pastry-crust, that was the wall;
The windows were made of black-pudding and white,
And slated with pancakes—you ne'er saw the like.

(1805.)

XL

Three young rats with black felt hats,
Three young ducks with white straw 'flats,'
Three young dogs with curling tails,
Three young cats with demi-veils,
Went out to walk with two young pigs
In satin vests and sorrel wigs.
But suddenly it chanced to rain,
And so they all went home again.

(1932.)

XLI

Robin the Bobbin, the big-bellied Ben,
He ate more meat than fourscore men;
He ate a cow, he ate a calf,
He ate a butcher and a half,
He ate a church, he ate a steeple,
He ate the priest and all the people!

(1744 and 1842.)

XLII

Rub-a-dub-dub,
Three men in a tub,
And how do you think they got there?
The butcher, the baker,
The candlestick maker,
They all jumped out of a rotten potater—
'Twas enough to make a man stare!

(1798 and 1830.)

XLIII

I saw a ship a-sailing
A-sailing on the sea,
And oh but it was laden
With pretty things for me.

There were comfits in the cabin,
And apples in the hold;
The sails were made of silk,
And the masts were all of gold.

The four-and-twenty sailors
That stood between the decks,
Were four and twenty white mice
With chains about their necks.

The captain was a duck
    With a packet on his back,
And when the ship began to move
    The captain said: 'Quack! quack!'

(1846.)

XLIV

Solomon Grundy,
Born on a Monday,
Christened on Tuesday,
Married on Wednesday,
Took ill on Thursday,
Worse on Friday,
Died on Saturday,
Buried on Sunday—
And that was the end of Solomon Grundy.

(1842.)

XLV

Sing a song of sixpence,
    A pocket full of rye;
Four and twenty blackbirds
    Baked in a pie.

When the pie was opened
    The birds began to sing;
Was not that a dainty dish
    To set before the king.

The king was in his counting-house
    Counting out his money;
The queen was in the parlour
    Eating bread and honey.

The maid was in the garden
   Hanging out the clothes,
There came a little blackbird
   And snapt off her nose.

Jenny was so mad,
   She didn't know what to do;
She put her finger in her ear,
   And crackt it right in two.

(1744 and 1842.)

XLVI

There was a man of Thessaly,
   And he was wondrous wise,
He jumped into a bramble bush
   And scratched out both his eyes.
And when he saw his eyes were out,
   With all his might and main
He jumped into another bush
   And scratched them in again.

(1744.)

XLVII

There was an old woman tossed up in a basket
Seventeen times as high as the Moon;
Where she was going I couldn't but ask it,
For in her hand she carried a broom.
'Old woman, old woman, old woman,' quoth I,
'Where are you going to, up so high?'
'To sweep the cobwebs from the sky!'
'May I go with you?'   'Yes, by-and-by.'

(1765.)

XLVIII

There was an old woman who lived in a shoe,
She had so many children she didn't know what to do.
She gave them some broth without any bread,
She borrowed a beetle and knocked them down dead,
Then she whipped them all soundly and sent them to bed.

(1784, etc.)

XLIX

There was a crooked man, and he went a crooked mile,
He found a crooked sixpence against a crooked stile;
He bought a crooked cat, which caught a crooked mouse,
And they all lived together in a little crooked house.

(1842.)

L

There was a little guinea-pig,
Who, being little, was not big;
He always walked upon his feet,
And never fasted when he did eat.

When from a place he ran away,
He never at that place did stay;
And while he ran, as I am told,
He ne'er stood still for young or old.

He often squeaked both loud and vi'lent,
And when he squeaked he ne'er was silent;
Though ne'er instructed by a cat,
He knew a mouse was not a rat.

One day, as I am certified,
He took a whim and fairly died;
And, as I 'm told by men of sense,
He never has been living since.   (1784.)

STRANGE SONGS AND POEMS

I

'MY LADY WENT TO CANTERBURY'

Nine mile to Michaelmas,
  Our dame began to brew;
Michael set his mare to grass,
  Lord, so fast it snew!

·   ·   ·   ·   ·

Yet I tell you mickle more:
  The cat lieth in the cradle;
I pray you keep true heart in store,
  A penny for a ladle.

·   ·   ·   ·   ·

Tirlery lorpin, the laverock sings,
  So merrily pipes the sparrow,
The cow broke loose, the rope ran home—
  Sir, God give you good-morrow!

Anonymous (c. 1550).

II

IF——

If all the world were paper,
  And all the sea were ink;
If all the trees were bread and cheese,
  How should we do for drink?

If all the world were sand,
  Oh then what should we lack'o?
If as they say there were no clay,
  How should we take tobacco?

If all our vessels ran,
  If none but had a crack;
If Spanish apes ate all the grapes,
  How should we do for sack?

If all the world were men,
  And men lived all in trenches,
And there were none but we alone,
  How should we do for wenches?

If friars had no bald pates,
  Nor nuns had no dark cloisters;
If all the seas were beans and peas,
  How should we do for oysters?

If all things were eternal,
  And nothing their end bringing;
If this should be, then how should we
  Here make an end of singing?

Anonymous (1641.)

III

NAMBY PAMBY

.   .   .   .   .

Namby Pamby's doubly mild,
Once a man and twice a child,
Now methinks I hear him say
Boys and girls come out to play,
Moon does shine as bright as day.
Now my Namby Pamby's found
Sitting on the Friar's ground,
Picking silver, picking gold,
Namby Pamby's never old.
Bally-cally they begin,
Namby Pamby still keeps in.
Namby Pamby is no clown,
London Bridge is broken down:
Now he courts the gay ladee,
Dancing o'er the Lady-lee:
Now he sings the lick-spit liar
Burning in the brimstone fire;
Liar, liar, lick-spit, lick,
Turn about the candle-stick.
Now he sings of Jacky Horner
Sitting in the chimney corner,
Eating of a Christmas pie,
Putting in his thumb, oh, fie!
Putting in, oh, fie! his thumb,
Pulling out, oh, strange! a plum.

.   .   .   .   .

Henry Carey (1725.)

IV

COCK ROBIN

Who killed Cock Robin?
  'I,' said the Sparrow,
  'With my bow and arrow,
I killed Cock Robin.'

Who saw him die?
  'I,' said the Fly,
  'With my little eye,
I saw him die.'

Who caught his blood?
  'I,' said the Fish,
  'With my little dish,
I caught his blood.'

Who 'll make the shroud?
  'I,' said the Beetle,
  'With my thread and needle,
I 'll make the shroud.'

Who 'll dig his grave?
  'I,' said the Owl,
  'With my pick and trowel,
I 'll dig his grave.'

Who 'll be the parson?
  'I,' said the Rook,
  'With my little book,
I 'll be the parson.'

Who 'll be the clerk?
  'I,' said the Lark,
  'If it 's not in the dark,
I 'll be the clerk.'

Who 'll carry the link?
  'I,' said the Linnet,
  'I 'll fetch it in a minute,
I 'll carry the link.'

Who 'll be chief mourner?
  'I,' said the Dove,
  'I 'll mourn for my love,
I 'll be chief mourner.'

Who 'll carry the coffin?
  'I,' said the Kite,
  'If it 's not through the night,
I 'll carry the coffin.'

Who 'll bear the pall?
  'We,' said the Wren,
  Both the cock and the hen,
'We 'll bear the pall.'

Who 'll sing a psalm?
  'I,' said the Thrush,
  As he sat on a bush,
'I 'll sing a psalm.'

Who 'll toll the bell?
  'I,' said the Bull,
  'Because I can pull,
I 'll toll the bell.'

All the birds in the air
   Fell a-sighin' and a-sobbin'
When they heard the bell toll
   For poor Cock Robin.

Anonymous (1744, etc.).

V

THE LITTLE OLD WOMAN

There was an old woman, as I 've heard tell,
She went to market, her eggs for to sell;
She went to market all on a market day,
And she fell asleep on the king's highway.

There came by a pedlar whose name was Stout,
He cut her petticoats all round about;
He cut her petticoats up to the knees,
Which made the old woman to shiver and freeze.

When this little woman first did wake,
She began to shiver and she began to shake,
She began to wonder and she began to cry:
'Oh deary, deary me, this is none of I!

'But if it be I, as I do hope it be,
I 've a little dog at home and he 'll know me;
And if it be I, he 'll wag his little tail,
And if it be not I, he 'll loudly bark and wail.'

Home went the little woman all in the dark,
Up got the little dog, and he began to bark;
He began to bark, so she began to cry:
'Oh deary, deary me, this is none of I!'

Anonymous (1775 and 1842).

VI

ON A PACK OF CARDS

The Queen of Hearts,
She made some tarts,
All on a summer's day.
The Knave of Hearts
He stole those tarts,
And with them ran away.
The King of Hearts
Called for those tarts,
And beat the Knave full sore;
The Knave of Hearts
Brought back those tarts,
And said he 'd ne'er steal more.

The King of Spades,
He kissed the maids,
Which vexed the Queen full sore;
The Queen of Spades
She beat those maids,
And turned them out of door:
The Knave of Spades
Grieved for these jades,
And did for them implore;
The Queen so gent,
She did relent,
And vowed she 'd ne'er strike more.

The King of Clubs
He often drubs
His loving Queen and wife;

The Queen of Clubs
Returns him snubs,
And all is noise and strife:
The Knave of Clubs
Gives winks and rubs,
And swears he 'll take her part;
For when our kings
Will do such things
They should be made to smart.

The Diamond King
I fain would sing,
And likewise his fair Queen,
But that the Knave,
A naughty slave,
Must needs step in between.
Good Diamond King
With hempen string
This haughty Knave destroy,
Then may your Queen
With mind serene
Your royal state enjoy.

Anonymous (1782).

VII

OLD MOTHER HUBBARD AND HER DOG

Old Mother Hubbard
Went to the cupboard,
To fetch her poor dog a bone;
But when she got there
The cupboard was bare,
And so the poor dog had none.

She went to the baker's
To buy him some bread;
But when she came back
The poor dog was dead.

She went to the undertaker's
To buy him a coffin;
But when she came back
The poor dog was laughin'.

She took a clean dish
To get him some tripe;
But when she came back
He was smoking a pipe.

She went to the alehouse
To get him some beer;
But when she came back
The dog sat in a chair.

She went to the tavern
For wine white and red;
But when she came back
The dog stood on his head.

She went to the fruiterer's
 To buy him some fruit;
But when she came back
 He was playing the flute.

She went to the tailor's
 To buy him a coat;
But when she came back
 He was riding a goat.

She went to the hatter's,
 To buy him a hat;
But when she came back
 He was feeding the cat.

She went to the barber's
 To buy him a wig;
But when she came back
 He was dancing a jig.

She went to the cobbler's
 To buy him some shoes;
But when she came back
 He was reading the news.

She went to the seamstress
 To buy him some linen;
But when she came back
 The dog was a-spinnin'.

She went to the hosier's
 To buy him some hose;
But when she came back
 He was dressed in his clothes.

The dame made a curtsy,
  The dog made a bow;
The dame said: 'Your servant.'
  The dog said: 'Bow-wow!'

Sarah Catherine Martin (1805).

VIII

THE BUTTERFLY'S BALL

'Come take up your hats and away let us haste
To the Butterfly's Ball and the Grasshopper's feast.
The Trumpeter, Gad-fly, has summoned the crew,
And the revels are now only waiting for you!'
So said little Robert, and pacing along,
His merry companions came forth in a throng.

And on the smoothe grass, by the side of a wood,
Beneath a broad oak that for ages had stood,
Saw the children of earth and the tenants of air
For an evening's amusement together repair.
And there came the Beetle, so blind and so black,
Who carried the Emmet, his friend, on his back.
And there was the Gnat and the Dragonfly too,
With all their relations, green, orange, and blue.
And there came the Moth with his plumage of down,
And the Hornet in jacket of yellow and brown;
Who with him the Wasp, his companion, did bring,
But they promised that evening to lay by their sting.
And the sly little Dormouse crept out of his hole,
And brought to the feast his blind brother the Mole.
And the Snail, with his horns peeping out of his shell,
Came from a great distance—the length of an ell.
    A mushroom their table, and on it was laid
A water-dock leaf, which a table-cloth made.
The viands were various, to each of their taste,
And the Bee brought her honey to crown the repast.
    Then close on his haunches, so solemn and wise,
The Frog, from a corner, looked up to the skies.

And the Squirrel, well pleased such diversions to see,
Mounted high overhead and looked down from a tree.
Then out came the Spider with finger so fine,
To show his dexterity on the tight line.
From one branch to another his cobwebs he slung,
Then quick as an arrow he darted along;
But just in the middle—oh, shocking to tell!—
From his rope in an instant poor Harlequin fell.
Yet he touched not the ground, but with talons outspread
Hung suspended in air at the end of a thread.
  Then the Grasshopper came with a jerk and a spring,
Very long was his leg, though but short was his wing:
He took but three leaps, and was soon out of sight,
Then chirped his own praises the rest of the night.
  With step so majestic the Snail did advance
And promised the gazers a minuet to dance.
But they all laughed so loud that he pulled in his head,
And went in his own little chamber to bed.
  Then, as evening gave way to the shadows of night,
Their watchman, the Glow-worm, came out with a light.

'Then home let us hasten, while yet we can see,
For no watchman is waiting for you and for me.'
  So said little Robert, and pacing along,
His merry companions returned in a throng.

William Roscoe (1808).

see page 196

The King of Spades, he kissed the maids

IX

AIKEN DRUM

There was a man lived in the Moon, lived in the Moon,
   lived in the Moon;
There was a man lived in the Moon—
   And his name was Aiken Drum!

And his hat was made of good cream cheese,
And his coat was made of good roast beef,
And his buttons were made of penny loaves,
And his waistcoat was made of crust of pies,
And his breeches were made of haggis bags—
   And his name was Aiken Drum!

   And he played upon a ladle, a ladle, a ladle,
   And he played upon a ladle,
      And his name was Aiken Drum.

There was a man lived in our town, lived in our town,
   lived in our town;
There was a man lived in our town,
   And his name was Willy Wood!

And he ate up all the good cream cheese,
And he ate up all the good roast beef,
And he ate up all the penny loaves,
And he ate up all the crust of pies,
But he choked upon the haggis bags—
   And his name was Willy Wood!

   And he played upon a razor, a razor, a razor;
   And he played upon a razor,
      And his name was Willy Wood.

                              Anonymous (before 1821).

X

DAME WIGGINS OF LEE AND HER WONDERFUL CATS

Dame Wiggins of Lee was a worthy old soul
As e'er threaded a needle or washed in a bowl:
She held mice and rats in such antipathy
That seven fine Cats kept Dame Wiggins of Lee.

While to make a nice pudding she went for a sparrow,
They were wheeling a sick lamb home in a barrow.
'You shall all have some sprats for your humanity,
My seven good Cats!' said Dame Wiggins of Lee.

She wished them good night, and went up to bed:
When lo! in the morning the Cats were all fled.
The Dame's heart was nigh broke, so she sat down to weep:
When she saw them come back, each riding a sheep.

The Farmer soon heard where his sheep went astray,
And arrived at Dame's door with his faithful dog Tray.
For their kindness he had them all drawn by his team;
And he gave them some field-mice, and raspberry cream.

For the care of his Lamb, and their comical pranks,
He gave them a ham, and abundance of thanks.
'Now come in to supper, and sit down with me:
All welcome, once more!' cried Dame Wiggins of Lee.

Richard Scrafton Sharpe (1823).

XI

THE WISE MEN OF GOTHAM

In a bowl to sea went wise men three,
    On a brilliant night of June:
They carried a net, and their hearts were set
    On fishing up the Moon.

The sea was calm, the air was balm,
    Not a breath stirred low or high,
And the Moon, I trow, lay as bright below,
    And as round as in the sky.

The wise men with the current went,
    Nor paddle nor oar had they,
And still as the grave they went on the wave,
    That they might not disturb their prey.

Far, far at sea were the wise men three,
    When their fishing net they threw;
And at their throw the Moon below
    In a thousand fragments flew.

They drew in their net, it was empty and wet,
    And they had lost their pain,
Soon ceased the play of each dancing ray,
    And the image was round again.

Three times they threw, three times they drew,
    And all the while were mute;
And ever anew their wonder grew,
    Till they could not but dispute.

The three wise men got home again
   To their children and their wives:
But touching their trip and their net's vain dip
   They disputed all their lives.

The wise men three could never agree
   Why they missed their promised boon;
They agreed alone that their net they had thrown,
   And they had not caught the Moon.

Thomas Love Peacock (1825).

XII

POP GOES THE WEASEL

Up and down the City Road,
In and out the Eagle;
That 's the way the money goes—
Pop goes the weasel!

Half a pound of tuppenny rice,
Half a pound of treacle;
Mix it up and make it nice—
Pop goes the weasel!

Every night when I go out;
The monkey 's on the table;
Take a stick and knock it off—
Pop gocs the weasel!

Anonymous (before 1855).

XIII

NURSERY NONSENSE

I

There lived an old man in a garret,
    So afraid of a little tom-cat,
That he pulled himself up to the ceiling,
    And hung himself up in his hat.

And for fear of the wind and the rain
    He took his umbrella to bed—
I 've half an idea that silly old man
    Was a little bit wrong in his head.

2

An inquisitive Cock Sparrow
    Asked every man in Wales,
Why Parrots had long noses,
    And Foxes had long tails.

Some said that Foxes used their tails
    In winter for a muff;
And Parrots' noses all were long,
    Because they all took snuff.

But the reason, so it seems to me,
    As perhaps it will to you,
Is that they once tried short tails,
    And short tails wouldn't do.

3

Two little Dogs went out for a walk,
  And it was windy weather,
So for fear the wind should blow them away,
  They tied their tails together.

They tied their tails with a yard of tape,
  And the wind it blew and blew
As sharp and keen as a carving-knife,
  And cut the tape in two.

And away and away, like kites in the air
  Those two little Dogs flew about,
Till one little Dog was blown to bits,
  And the other turned inside out.

4

In London-town Dame Trottypeg
   Lived high up in a garret,
And with her lived a wee pet Dog,
   A Tom-cat, and a Parrot.

A cleverer or a funnier Dog
   I 'm sure you never saw;
For, like a sailor, he could dance
   A hornpipe on one paw.

And all the while the Doggie danced,
   That Pussy-cat was able
Just like a flute to play his tail
   Upon the kitchen table.

But what a tongue, and O what brains
  Were in that Parrot's head!
It took two men to understand
  One half the things he said.

D'Arcy Wentworth Thompson (1864).

XIV

TOPSY-TURVY WORLD

I

If the butterfly courted the bee,
   And the owl the porcupine;
If churches were built in the sea,
   And three times one was nine;
If the pony rode his master,
   If buttercups ate the cows,
If the cat had the dire disaster
   To be worried, sir, by the mouse;
If mamma, sir, sold the baby
   To the gipsy for half a crown;
If a gentleman, sir, was a lady—
   The world would be Upside-Down!
If any or all these wonders
   Should ever come about,
I should not consider them blunders,
   For I should be Inside-Out!

2

Ba-ba, black wool,
   Have you any sheep?
Yes, sir, a pack-full,
   Creep, mouse, creep!
Four and twenty little maids
   Hanging out the pie,
Out jumped the honey-pot,
   Guy-Fawkes, Guy!

Cross-latch, cross-latch,
  Sit and spin the fire,
When the pie was opened
  The bird was on the briar!

3

Carry and Kate
Swallowed a slate:
David and Dick
Lived in a stick:
Hetty and Helen
Said: 'Oh, what a dwellin'!'
Patty and Prue
Took baths in a flue:
Nathan and Ned
Caught fish in their bed;
Nothing could hide 'em,
And Dorothy fried 'em.
This was on Tuesday,
Which always was news day.

4

'If black was white,
  And white was black,
I would swallow a light
  And live in a sack,
And swim on a kite'—
  Says jolly Jack.
                William Brighty Rands (1864).

XV

SING-SONG VERSES

When fishes set umbrellas up
  If the rain-drops run,
Lizards will want their parasols
  To shade them from the sun.

The peacock has a score of eyes,
  With which he cannot see;
The cod-fish has a silent sound,
  However that may be.

No dandelions tell the time,
  Although they turn to clocks;
Cat's cradle does not hold the cat,
  Nor foxglove fit the fox.

Christina Rossetti (1872).

XVI

A QUADRUPEDREMIAN SONG

He dreamt that he saw the Buffalant,
  And the spottified Dromedaraffe,
The blue Camelotamus, lean and gaunt,
  And the wild Tigeroceros calf.

The maned Liodillo loudly roared,
  And the Peccarbok whistled its whine,
The Chinchayak leapt on the dewy sward,
  As it hunted the pale Baboopine.

He dreamt that he met the Crocoghau,
  As it swam in the Stagnolent Lake;
But everything that in dreams he saw
  Came of eating too freely of cake.

Tom Hood (1875).

XVII

MONTEZUMA

Montezuma
Met a puma
Coming through the rye;
Montezuma
Made the puma
Into apple-pie.

Invitation
To the nation
Everyone to come.
Montezuma
And the puma
Give a kettle-drum.

Acceptation
Of the nation,
One and all invited.
Montezuma
And the puma
Equally delighted.

Preparation,
Ostentation,
Dresses rich prepared:
Feathers—jewels—
Work in crewels—
No expense is spared.

Congregation
Of the nation
Round the palace wall.
Awful rumour
That the puma
Won't be served at all.

Deputation
From the nation,
Audience they gain.
'What 's this rumour?
Montezuma,
If you please, explain.'

Montezuma
(Playful humour
Very well sustained)
Answers 'Pie-dish,
And it 's my dish,
Is for me retained.'

Exclamation!
Indignation!
Feeling running high.
Montezuma
Joins the puma
In the apple-pie.

D. F. Alderson (1895).

XVIII

AN UNEXPECTED FACT

If down his throat a man should choose
    In fun, to jump or slide,
He 'd scrape his shoes against his teeth,
    Nor soil his own inside.
But if his teeth were lost and gone,
And not a stump to scrape upon,
He 'd see at once how very pat
His tongue lay there, by way of mat,
And he would wipe his feet on *that*!

Edward Cannon (1897).

XIX

TAME ANIMALS I HAVE KNOWN

A thick-fleeced lamb came trotting by:
'Pray whither now, my lamb,' quoth I.
'To have,' said he with ne'er a stop,
'My wool clipped at the baa-baa shop.'

I asked the dog: 'Why all this din?'
Said he: 'I'm fashioned outside in,
And all my days and nights I've tried
My best to get the bark outside.'

A hen was cackling loud and long,
Said I to her: 'How strange your song!'
Said she: ''Tis scarce a song; in fact
It is a lay, to be eggs-act.'

I asked the cat: 'Pray tell me why
You love to sing?'   She blinked her eye.
'My purr-puss, sir, as you can see,
Is to a-mews myself,' said she.

A horse was being lashed one day.
Said I: 'Why don't you run away?'
'Neigh, neigh! my stable mind,' said he,
'Still keeps its equine-imity.'

I asked the cow: 'Why don't you kick
The man who whips you with the stick?'
'Alas I must be lashed,' said she,
'That I may give whipped cream, you see!'

Nixon Waterman (1904).

XX

THE FISHERMAN ON TOAST

The Sardine was lurking behind in the tin
  To smooth his young whiskers in oil,
Whilst his sister was fanning the flames with her fin
  In hopes that the kettle would boil.
The Shrimp and the Pilchard had changed a bank-note
  To pay the old Salmon his debt,
When the black-hearted fisherman came in his boat
  And scooped up the lot in his net.

The callow young Bloater was darning a frill,
  The Gurnet was trolling for grouse,
The Lobster was mildly dissuading the Brill
  From the folly of building a house.
The Mackerel was tossing about in his bed
  And dreaming of parsley and cooks,
And the black-hearted fisherman smiled as he said:
  'I can catch all these fellows on hooks!'

A Storm-Cloud the size of an extra large bat
  Came walloping out of the west,
He was thick as a waterproof, black as a hat,
  And he hugged the cold hail to his breast.
He burst o'er the black-hearted fisherman's head
  When he caught him five miles from the coast,
Then the kind-hearted Cloud as he got into bed
Rejoiced that those dear little fishes were fed
  On fisherman served up on toast.
        Edward Abbott Parry (1907).

XXI

HILDEBRAND

'Oh, Murder!   What was that, Papa?'
'My child, it was a Motor-Car,
  A Most Ingenious Toy!
Designed to Captivate and Charm
Much rather than to rouse Alarm
  In any English Boy.

'What would your Great Grandfather who
Was Aide-de-Camp to General Brue,
And lost a leg at Waterloo,
And Quatre-Bras, and Ligny too!
  And died at Trafalgar!—
What would he have remarked to hear
His Young Descendant shriek with fear,
Because he happened to be near
  A Harmless Motor-Car!

'But do not fret about it!   Come!
We 'll off to Town and purchase some!'

Hilaire Belloc (1907).

XXII

LINES AND SQUARES

Whenever I walk in a London street,
I 'm ever so careful to watch my feet;
   And I keep in the squares,
   And the masses of bears,
Who wait at the corners all ready to eat
The sillies who tread on the lines of the street,
   Go back to their lairs,
   And I say to them, 'Bears,
Just look how I 'm walking in all of the squares!'

And the little bears growl to each other, 'He 's mine,
As soon as he 's silly and steps on a line.'
And some of the bigger bears try to pretend
That they came round the corner to look for a friend;
And they try to pretend that nobody cares
Whether you walk on the lines or squares.

But only the sillies believe their talk;
It 's ever so 'portant how you walk.
And it 's ever so jolly to call out, 'Bears,
Just watch me walking in all the squares!'

A. A. Milne (1924).

XXIII

HUMS OF POOH

I

On Monday, when the sun is hot,
I wonder to myself a lot:
'Now is it true, or is it not,
That what is which and which is what?'

On Tuesday, when it hails and snows,
The feeling on me grows and grows
That hardly anybody knows
If those are these or these are those.

On Wednesday, when the sky is blue,
And I have nothing else to do,
I sometimes wonder if it 's true
That who is what and what is who.

On Thursday, when it starts to freeze
And hoar-frost twinkles on the trees,
Now very readily one sees
That these are whose—but whose are these?

2

Cottleston, Cottleston, Cottleston Pie!
A fly can't bird, but a bird can fly—
A fish can't whistle and neither can I—
Why does a chicken, I don't know why!
Ask me a riddle, and I reply:
'*Cottleston, Cottleston, Cottleston Pie!*'

A. A. Milne (1926).

XXIV

AWAKE, MY LUTE!

I stood in the gloom of a spacious room
    Where I listened for hours (on and off)
To a terrible bore with a beard like a snore
    And a heavy rectangular cough,
Who discoursed on the habits of orchids and rabbits
    And how an electron behaves
And a way to cure croup with solidified soup
    In a pattern of circular waves;
Till I suddenly spied that what stood at his side
    Was a richly upholstered baboon
With paws like the puns in a poem of Donne's
    And a tail like a voyage to the Moon.
Then I whispered, 'Look out! For I very much doubt
    If your colleague is really a man.'
But the lecturer said, without turning his head,
    'Oh, that's only the Beverage plan!'
As one might have forseen, the whole sky became green
    At this most injudicious remark,
For the Flood had begun and we both had to run
    For our place in the queue to the Ark.
Then, I hardly know how (we were swimming by now),
    The sea got all covered with scum
Made of publishers' blurbs and irregular verbs
    Of the kind which have datives in -um;
And the waves were so high that far up in the sky
    We saw the grand lobster, and heard
How he snorted, 'Compare the achievements of Blair
    With the grave of King Alfred the Third,

And add a brief note and if possible quote,
   And distinguish and trace and discuss
The probable course of a Methodist horse
   When it 's catching a decimal bus.'
My answer was Yes.   But they marked it N.S.,
   And a truffle-fish grabbed at my toe,
And dragged me deep down to a bombulous town
   Where the traffic was silent and slow.
Then a voice out of heaven observed, 'Quarter past seven!'
   And I threw all the waves off my head,
For the voice beyond doubt was the voice of my scout,
   And the bed of that sea was my bed.

C. S. Lewis (1943).

THE SURPRISING ADVENTURES OF
BARON MUNCHAUSEN

I

I SET off from Rome on a journey to Russia, in the midst of winter, from a just notion that frost and snow must of course mend the roads, which every traveller had described as uncommonly bad through the northern parts of Germany, Poland, Courland, and Livonia.   I went on horse-back, as the most convenient manner of travelling.   I was but lightly clothed, and of this I felt the inconvenience the more I advanced north-east.

I went on: night and darkness overtook me.   No village was to be seen.   The country was covered with snow, and I was unacquainted with the road.

Tired, I alighted, and fastened my horse to something like a pointed stump of a tree which appeared above the snow; for the sake of safety I placed my pistols under my arm and lay down on the snow, where I slept so soundly that I did not open my eyes till full daylight.   It is not easy to conceive my astonishment to find myself in the midst of a village, lying in a churchyard; nor was my horse to be seen, but I heard him soon after neigh somewhere above me.   On looking upwards, I beheld him hanging by his bridle to the weather-cock of the steeple.   Matters were now very plain to me: the village had been covered with snow overnight; a sudden change of weather had taken place.   I had sunk down to the churchyard whilst asleep, gently, and in the same pro-portion as the snow had melted away, and what in the dark

I had taken to be a stump of a little tree appearing above the snow, to which I had tied my horse, proved to have been the cross or weathercock of the steeple!

Without long consideration I took one of my pistols, shot the bridle in two, brought down the horse, and proceeded on my journey.

He carried me well. Advancing into the interior parts of Russia, I found travelling on horseback rather unfashionable in winter; therefore I submitted, as I always do, to the custom of the country, took a single-horse sledge and drove briskly towards St Petersburg. I do not exactly recollect whether it was in Eastland or Jugemanland, but I remember that in the midst of a dreary forest I spied a terrible wolf making after me, with all the speed of ravenous winter hunger. He soon overtook me. There was no possibility of escape. Mechanically I laid myself down flat in the sledge and let my horse run for our safety. What I wished, but hardly hoped or expected, happened immediately after. The wolf did not mind me in the least, but took a leap over me, and falling furiously on the horse, began instantly to tear and devour the hind part of the poor animal, which ran the faster for his pain and terror. Thus unnoticed and safe myself, I lifted my head slyly up, and with horror I beheld that the wolf had ate his way into the horse's body. It was not long before he had fairly forced himself into it, when I took my advantage and fell upon him with the butt-end of my whip. This unexpected attack in his rear frightened him so much that he leaped forward with all his might; the horse's carcass dropped on the ground, but in his place the wolf was in the harness, and I on my part whipping him continually, we both arrived in full career safe in St Petersburg, contrary to our respective expectations, and very much to the astonishment of the spectators.

II

One morning I saw through the windows of my bedroom that a large pond, not far off, was covered with wild ducks. In an instant I took my gun from the corner, ran downstairs and out of the house in such a hurry that I imprudently struck my face against the door-post. Fire flew out of my eyes, but it did not prevent my intention. I soon came within shot, when, levelling my piece, I observed, to my sorrow, that even the flint had sprung from the cock, by the violence of the shock I had just received. There was no time to be lost. I presently remembered the effect it had upon my eyes, therefore opened the pan, levelled my piece against the wild fowls, and my fist against one of my eyes. A hearty blow drew sparks again; the shot went off, and I killed fifty brace of ducks, twenty widgeons, and three couple of teals. Presence of mind is the soul of manly exercises. If soldiers and sailors owe to it many of their lucky escapes, hunters and sportsmen are not less beholden to it for many of their successes. In a noble forest in Russia I met a fine black fox, whose valuable skin it would have been a pity to tear by ball or shot. Reynard stood close to a tree. In a twinkling I took out my ball and placed a good spike nail in its room, fired, and hit him so cleverly that I nailed his brush fast to the tree. I now went up to him, took out my hanger, gave him a cross cut over the face, laid hold of my whip and fairly flogged him out of his fine skin.

Chance and good luck often correct our mistakes: of this I had a singular instance soon after, when, in the depth of a forest, I saw a wild pig and sow running close behind each other. My ball had missed them, yet the foremost pig only ran away, and the sow stood motionless, as fixed to the ground. On examining into the matter I found the latter

see page 242

'I then jumped over a hedge about nine feet high'

one to be an old sow, blind with age, which had taken hold of
her pig's tail, in order to be led along by filial duty.   My
ball, having passed between the two, had cut his leading-
string, which the old sow continued to hold in her mouth;
and as her former guide did not draw her on any longer, she
had stopped, of course.   I therefore laid hold of the
remaining end of the pig's tail and led the old beast home,
without any further trouble on my part, and without any
reluctance or apprehension on the part of the helpless old
animal.

Terrible as these wild sows are, yet more fierce and dangerous are the boars, one of which I had once the misfortune
to meet in a forest, unprepared for attack or defence.   I retired behind an oak-tree just when the furious animal levelled
a side-blow at me with such force that his tusks pierced
through the tree, by which means he could neither repeat the
blow nor retire.   'Ho! ho!' thought I, 'I shall soon have
you now,' and immediately I laid hold of a stone, wherewith
I hammered and bent his tusks in such a manner that he
could not retreat by any means, and must wait my return
from the next village, whither I went for ropes and a cart to
secure him properly, and to carry him off safe and alive, in
which I perfectly succeeded.

III

Having one day spent all my shot, I found myself unexpectedly in the presence of a stately stag, looking at me as
unconcernedly as if he had known of my empty pouches.
I charged immediately with powder, and upon it a good
handful of cherry-stones, for I had sucked the fruit as far as
the hurry would permit.   Thus I let fly at him, and hit him
just on the middle of the forehead, between his antlers: it

stunned him—he staggered—yet he made off.   A year or two after, being with a party in the same forest, I beheld a noble stag with a fine full-grown cherry-tree above ten feet high between his antlers.   I immediately recollected my former adventure, looked upon him as my property, and brought him to the ground by one shot, which at once gave me the haunch and cherry-sauce; for the tree was covered with the richest fruit, the like I never had tasted before.

Daylight and powder were spent one day in a Polish forest.   When I was going home a terrible bear made up to me in great speed with open mouth, ready to fall upon me. All my pockets were searched in an instant for powder and ball, but in vain; I found nothing but two spare flints: one I flung with all my might into the monster's open jaws, down his throat.   It gave him pain and made him turn about, so that I could level the second at his back door, which, indeed, I did with wonderful success; for it flew in, met the first flint in the stomach, struck fire, and blew up the bear with a terrible explosion.   Though I came safe off that time, yet I should not wish to try it again, or venture against bears with no other ammunition.

There is a kind of fatality in it.   The fiercest and most dangerous animals generally came upon me when defence-less, as if they had a notion or an instinctive intimation of it. Thus a frightful wolf rushed upon me so suddenly and so close that I could do nothing but follow mechanical instinct, and thrust my fist into his open mouth.   For safety's sake I pushed on and on, till my arm was fairly in up to the shoulder.   How should I disengage myself?   I was not much pleased with my awkward situation—with a wolf face to face—our ogling was not of the most pleasant kind.   If I withdrew my arm, then the animal would fly the more furiously upon me; that I saw in his flaming eyes.   In short,

I laid hold of his entrails, turned him inside out like a glove, and flung him to the ground, where I left him.

The same expedient would not have answered against a mad dog, which soon after came running against me in a narrow street in St Petersburg. Run who can, I thought; and to do this the better I threw off my fur cloak and was safe within doors in an instant. I sent my servant for the cloak, and he put it in the wardrobe with my other clothes. The day after I was amazed and frightened by Jack's bawling: 'For God's sake, sir, your fur cloak is mad!' I hastened up to him, and found almost all my clothes tossed about and torn to pieces. The fellow was perfectly right in his apprehensions about the fur cloak's madness. I saw him myself just then falling upon a fine full-dress suit, which he shook and tossed in an unmerciful manner.

IV

All these narrow and lucky escapes, gentlemen, were chances turned to advantage by presence of mind and vigorous exertions, which, taken together, as everybody knows, make the fortunate sportsman, sailor, and soldier; but he would be a very blameable and imprudent sportsman, admiral, or general who would always depend upon chance and his stars, without troubling himself about those arts which are their particular pursuits, and without providing the very best implements which ensure success. I was not blameable either way; for I have always been as remarkable for the excellency of my horses, dogs, guns, and swords, as for the proper manner of using and managing them; so that upon the whole I may hope to be remembered in the forest, upon the turf, and in the field. I shall not enter here into any detail of my stables, kennel, or armoury; but I remember with pleasure and tenderness a superb Lithuanian horse, which no money could have bought. He became mine by an accident, which gave me an opportunity of showing my horsemanship to a great advantage. I was at Count Przobossky's noble country seat in Lithuania, and remained with the ladies at tea in the drawing-room while the gentlemen were down in the yard to see a young horse of blood, which was just arrived from the stud. We suddenly heard a noise of distress. I hastened downstairs, and found the horse so unruly that nobody durst approach or mount him. The most resolute horsemen stood dismayed and aghast: despondency was expressed in every countenance, when, in one leap, I was on his back, took him by surprise, and worked him quite into gentleness and obedience, with the best display of horsemanship I was master of. Fully to show this to the ladies, and save them unnecessary trouble, I forced him to leap in at one of the open windows of the tea-room, walked round several times, pace, trot, and gallop; and at last made him mount the tea-table, there to repeat his lessons, in a pretty style of miniature, which was exceedingly pleasing to the ladies, for he performed them amazingly well, and did not break either cup or saucer. It placed me so high in their opinion, and so well in that of the noble lord, that with his usual politeness he begged I would accept of this young horse, and ride him full career to conquest and honour, in the campaign against the Turks, which was soon to be opened, under the command of Count Munich.

We took the field, among several other reasons, it seems, with an intention to retrieve the character of the Russian arms, which had been blemished a little by Czar Peter's last campaign on the Pruth; and this we fully accomplished by several very fatiguing and glorious campaigns under the command of that great general I mentioned before.

Modesty forbids individuals to arrogate to themselves great successes or victories, the glory of which is generally engrossed by the commander. Nor do I claim any particular share of glory in the great engagements with the enemy. However, having had the command of a body of hussars, I went upon several expeditions with discretionary powers; and the success I then met with is, I think, fairly and only to be placed to my account, and to that of the brave fellows whom I led on to conquest and to victory.

We had very hot work once in the van of the army when we drove the Turks into Oczakow. My spirited Lithuanian had almost brought me into a scrape. I had an advanced fore-post and saw the enemy coming against me in a cloud of dust, which left me rather uncertain about their actual numbers and real intentions. To wrap myself up in a similar cloud was common prudence, but would not have much advanced my knowledge, or answered the end for which I had been sent out; therefore I let my flankers on both wings spread to the right and left, and make what dust they could, and I myself led on straight upon the enemy, to have a nearer sight of them. In this I was gratified, for they stood and fought till, for fear of my flankers, they began to move off rather disorderly. This was the moment to fall upon them with spirit. We broke them entirely, made a terrible havoc amongst them, and drove them not only back to a walled town in their rear, but even through it, contrary to our most sanguine expectations.

The swiftness of my Lithuanian enabled me to be foremost in the pursuit; and seeing the enemy fairly flying through the opposite gate, I thought it would be prudent to stop in the market-place, to order the men to rendezvous. I stopped, gentlemen; but judge of my astonishment when in this market-place I saw not one of my hussars about me!

Are they scouring the other streets; or what is become of them? They could not be far off, and must, at all events, soon join me. In that expectation I walked my panting Lithuanian to a spring in this market-place, and let him drink. He drank uncommonly—with an eagerness not to be satisfied, but natural enough, for when I looked round for my men, what should I see, gentlemen—the hind part of the poor creature's croup and legs were missing, as if he had been cut in two, and the water ran out as it came in, without refreshing or doing him any good! How it could have happened was quite a mystery to me, till I returned with him to the town gate. There I saw that, when I rushed in pell-mell with the flying enemy, they had dropped the portcullis, unperceived by me, which had totally cut off his hind part, that still lay quivering on the outside of the gate. It would have been an irreparable loss had not our farrier contrived to bring both parts together while hot. He sewed them up with sprigs and young shoots of laurels that were at hand; the wound healed, and, what could not have happened but to so glorious a horse, the sprigs took root in his body, grew up, and formed a bower over me, so that afterwards I could go upon many other expeditions in the shade of my own and my horse's laurels.

V

I was not always successful. I had the misfortune to be overpowered by numbers, to be made prisoner of war, and, what is worse, but always usual among the Turks, to be sold for a slave. In that state of humiliation my daily task was not very hard and laborious, but rather singular and irksome. It was to drive the Sultan's bees every morning to their pasture-grounds, to attend them all the day long, and against night to drive them back to their hives. One evening I missed a bee, and soon observed that two bears had fallen upon her, to tear her to pieces for the honey she carried. I had nothing like an offensive weapon in my hands but the silver hatchet which is the badge of the Sultan's gardeners and farmers. I threw it at the robbers, with an intention to frighten them away, and set the poor bee at liberty; but by an unlucky turn of my arm, it flew upwards, and continued rising till it reached the moon. How should I recover it? How fetch it down again? I recollected that turkey-beans grow very quick, and run up to an astonishing height. I planted one immediately; it grew, and actually fastened itself to one of the moon's horns. I had no more to do now but to climb up by it into the moon where I safely arrived, and had a troublesome piece of business before I could find my silver hatchet in a place where everything has the brightness of silver; at last, however, I found it in a heap of chaff and chopped straw. I was now for returning, but, alas! the heat of the sun had dried up my bean: it was totally useless for my descent; so I fell to work, and twisted me a rope of that chopped straw, as long and as well as I could make it. This I fastened to one of the moon's horns, and slid down to the end of it. Here I held myself fast with the left hand, and with the hatchet in my right I cut the long, now useless, end of the upper part, which, when tied to the lower end, brought me a good deal lower. This repeated splicing and tying of the rope did not improve its quality, or bring me down to the Sultan's farms. I was four or five miles from the earth at least when it broke. I fell to the ground with such amazing violence that I found myself stunned, and in a hole nine fathoms deep at least, made by the weight of my body falling from so great a height. I recovered, but knew not how to get out again; however, I dug slopes or steps with my nails, and easily accomplished it.

Peace was soon after concluded with the Turks; and, gaining my liberty, I left St Petersburg at the time of that singular revolution when the Emperor in his cradle, his mother, the Duke of Brunswick, her father, Field Marshal Munich, and many others were sent to Siberia. The winter was then so uncommonly severe all over Europe that ever since the sun seems to be frost-bitten. At my return to this place I felt on the road greater inconveniences than those I had experienced on my setting out.

I travelled post, and finding myself in a narrow lane bid the postilion give a signal with his horn, that other travellers might not meet us in the narrow passage. He blew with all his might, but his endeavours were in vain: he could not make the horn sound; which was unaccountable, and rather unfortunate, for soon after we found ourselves in the presence of another coach coming the other way. There was no proceeding. However, I got out of my carriage, and, being pretty strong, placed it, wheels and all, upon my head. I then jumped over a hedge about nine feet high (which, considering the weight of the coach, was rather difficult) into a field, and came out again by another jump into the road beyond the other carriage. I then went back for the horses, and placing one upon my head, and the other under my left arm, by the same means brought them to my coach, put to, and proceeded to an inn at the end of our stage. I should have told you that the horse under my arm was very spirited and not above four years old. In making my second spring over the hedge he expressed great dislike to that violent kind of motion, by kicking and snorting; however, I confined his hind-legs, by putting them into my coat pocket. After we arrived at the inn, my postilion and I refreshed ourselves: he hung his horn on a peg near the kitchen fire; I sat on the other side.

Suddenly we heard a *Tereng! tereng! teng! teng!* We looked round, and now found the reason why the postilion had not been able to sound his horn: his tunes were frozen up in the horn, and came out now by thawing, plain enough, and much to the credit of the driver; so that the honest fellow entertained us for some time with a variety of tunes without putting his mouth to the horn—*The King of Prussia's March, Over the Hill and over the Dale,* with many other favourite tunes.   At length the thawing entertainment concluded, as I shall this short account of my Russian travels.

Rudolph Erich Raspe (1785).

NONSENSE NUGGETS

———

I. OLD GREEK NONSENSE RHYMES

1

Little Hermogenes is so small
He can't reach anything down at all;
Though it's on the ground, he must let it lie—
For he's so short that it's still too high.

Lucilius (c. A.D. *50).*

2

Look at Marcus and take warning:
    Once he tried to win a race,
Ran all night, and in the morning
    Hadn't passed the starting place!

Lucilius.

3

Gaius was so very thin
    That his children, when he died,
On a box with nothing in
    Wrote: 'Dear Gaius is inside!'

Lucilius.

245

4

What 's come?   The end of Nikon's nose,
  But him I cannot see!
Run up the hill, and I suppose
In the far distance Nikon shows—
  He 'll be here presently!

                Nicarchus (*c.* A.D. 200).

5

I boiled hot water in an urn
  Till it was cold as ice;
I blew the fire to make it burn,
  Which froze it in a trice.

          After *Nicarchus* (*c.* A.D. 200).

II. SOME LIMERICKS

1

There was an Old Woman of Harrow
Who visited in a wheelbarrow,
   And her servant before
   Knock'd loud at each door
To announce the Old Woman of Harrow.

Anonymous (1821).

2

There was once a Young Man of Oporta
Who daily got shorter and shorter,
   The reason he said
   Was the hod on his head
Which was filled with the *heaviest* mortar.

Lewis Carroll (1845).

3

There was an Old Person of Diss,
Who said: 'It is this!   It is this!'
   When they said: 'What or which?'
   He jumped into a ditch,
Which absorbed that old person of Diss.

Edward Lear (uncollected).

4

There was a queer fellow named Woodin
Who always ate pepper with puddin',
   Till, one day, 'tis said,
   He sneezed off his head!
That imprudent old fellow named Woodin.

Cuthbert Bede (1868).

5

There was once a young Fir-tree of Bosnia
Which daily got ros'nier and ros'nier;
   It at last caught on fire
   And flamed higher and higher,
And the Angels said: 'My!   But that was near!'
       Dante Gabriel Rossetti (oral tradition).

6

There was a Young Lady of Riga
Who rode with a smile on a tiger;
   They returned from the ride
   With the lady inside,
And the smile on the face of the tiger.
       Anonymous (before 1888).

7

There was an Old Man of Toronto,
And people said: 'Where has he gone to?
   Here 's his table and chair,
   But *where* is he, where,
This invisible man of Toronto?'
       Andrew Lang (1888).

8

There was once a Young Lady of Ryde
Who ate a green apple and died;
   The apple fermented
   Inside the lamented,
And made cider inside her inside.
       Anonymous.

III. VARIOUS VERSES

1

SYLVAN CATCH

Buzz, quoth the blue fly,
  Hum, quoth the bee,
Buzz and hum they cry,
  And so do we.
In his ear, in his nose,
  Thus do you see;
He ate the dormouse,
  Else it was thee!

Ben Jonson (1616).

2

THE TURNIP SELLER

If a man who turnips cries,
Cry not when his father dies,
It is proof that he would rather
Have a turnip than his father.

Samuel Johnson (1786).

3

NONSENSE!

Higglety, pigglety, pop!
The dog has eaten the mop;
  The pig's in a hurry,
  The cat's in a flurry,
Higglety, pigglety, pop!

Samuel Goodrich (1846).

4
BETSINDA'S BUN

Oh, what fun
To have a plum bun!
How I wish it never was done!

W. M. Thackeray (1855).

5
CANNIBAL SONG

Choo a choo a choo tooth,
 Muntch, muntch.   Nycey!
Choo a choo a choo tooth,
 Muntch, muntch.   Nycey!

Charles Dickens (1868).

6
SOME CANNIBAL

If I were a Cassowary
 On the plains of Timbuctoo,
I would eat a missionary,
 Cassock, bands, and hymn-book, too.

Samuel Wilberforce (1805–73).

7
NOT I

Some like drink
In a pint pot,
Some like to think;
 Some not.

Strong Dutch cheese,
Old Kentucky rye,
Some like these:
    Not I.

Some like Poe,
And others like Scott,
Some like Mrs Stowe:
    Some not.

Some like to laugh,
Some like to cry,
Some like chaff;
    Not I.

Robert Louis Stevenson (1881).

8

A Sum

I give thee all, I can no more,
    Though small thy share may be:
Two halves, three thirds and quarters four
    Is all I bring to thee.

Lewis Carroll (1884).

9

A Race

A Daisy and a Buttercup
    Agreed to have a race,
A Squirrel was to be the judge
    A mile off from the place.

The Squirrel waited patiently
Until the day was done—
Perhaps he is there waiting still,
You see—they couldn't run.

Mrs Molesworth (1888).

10

THE GARDEN OF REGRETS

In the Garden of Regrets
Guinea-pigs are kept as pets,
    Even so!
But in Bedford Gardens, nay,
It is not at all the way,
    Sun or snow!

In the Garden of Regrets
There are lots of parroquets!
    Cockatoos!
Many and many a curious beast,
And they don't mind in the least
    Kangaroos!

Andrew Lang (1888).

11

DENNY MISQUOTES

'Come back!   Come back!' he cried in Greek
    Across the stormy water.
'And I'll forgive your Highland cheek,
    My daughter, O my daughter!'

E. Nesbit (1901).

12

DREAM VERSES

'Bachelor bears compare combine,
  To cheat me out of my mortal span;
They've had their dinner, and I want mine—
  And that is the difference,' said Timothy Bann.

E. Nesbit (1921).

13

MY GARDEN

I went down the garden, and what should I see
But an elephant's nest in a rhubarb tree;
And as I came in with an elephant's egg
I stepped on a snake which had only one leg.
But when the sun rose at the end of the day,
The snake and the elephant both flew away.

Roger Lancelyn Green (1956).

IV. 'LOOK TWICE' RHYMES

I

If we offend it is with our good will.
    That you should think we come not, to offend
But with good will.   To show our simple skill,
    That is the true beginning of our end.
Consider, then, we come but in despite,
    We do not come as minding to content you,
Our true intent is.   All for your delight
    We are not here.   That you should here repent you,
The actors are at hand; and, by their show,
You shall know all that you are like to know.

William Shakespeare (*c.* 1595).

2

I saw a peacock with a fiery tail
I saw a blazing comet drop down hail
I saw a cloud with ivy circled round
I saw a sturdy oak creep on the ground
I saw a pismire swallow up a whale
I saw a raging sea brim full of ale
I saw a Venice glass sixteen foot deep
I saw a well full of men's tears that weep
I saw their eyes all in a flame of fire
I saw a house big as the moon and higher
I saw the sun even in the midst of night
I saw the man who saw this wondrous sight.

Anonymous (1671).

3

Mollis abuti
Has an acuti,
No lasso finis,
Molli divinis.
Omi de armis tres,
Imi na dis tres
Cantu disco ver
Meas alo ver?

Jonathan Swift (c. 1730).

4

Every lady in this land
Has twenty nails upon each hand
Five and twenty on hands and feet
All this is true without deceit.

Traditional (collected c. 1789).

5

Infir taris,
Inoak nonis,
Inmudeelsis,
In claynonis.
Cana goateati vi?
Cana maretots?

Traditional (collected 1843).

6

Legomoton,
Acapon,
Alpha gheuse,
Pasti venison.

Traditional (collected 1845).

7

I saw a fish pond all on fire
I saw a house bow to a squire
I saw a parson twelve feet high
I saw a cottage in the sky
I saw a balloon made of lead
I saw a coffin drop down dead
I saw two sparrows run a race
I saw two horses making lace
I saw a girl just like a cat
I saw a kitten wear a hat
I saw a man who saw these too
And said though strange they all were true.

Traditional (collected 1889).

8

$$\frac{\text{Stand}}{\text{I}}\text{,}$$

$$\frac{\text{Take}}{\text{U}}\text{,}$$

$$\frac{\text{To}}{\text{Throw}}$$

$$\frac{\text{Taking}}{\text{My.}}$$

Traditional (oral).

9

Y Y U R,
Y Y U B,
I C U R
Y Y 4 me!

Traditional (oral).

10

There was once a young curate of Salisbury
Whose conduct was halisbury and scalisbury.
   One evening in Hampshire
   He took off his pampshire,
Though his vicar had told him to walisbury.

Traditional (oral).

V.   ORAL NONSENSE RHYMES

1

One fine day in the middle of the night
Two dead men got up to fight,
Two blind men to see fair play,
Two dumb men to shout 'Hurray!'
And two lame men to carry them away.

2

As I was coming down the stair
I met a man who wasn't there;
He wasn't there again to-day:
I *wish* that man would go away.

3

One fine October morning
   In September, last July,
The moon lay thick upon the ground,
   The snow shone in the sky;
The flowers were singing gaily
   And the birds were in full bloom,
I went down to the cellar
   To sweep the upstair room.

4

Weary Willie and tired Tim
Went to bed, but they couldn't get in.
So they sat on the ground
And had a look round—
Weary Willie and tired Tim.

5

As I was going out one day
My head fell off and rolled away.
But when I saw that it was gone,
I picked it up and put it on.

And when I got into the street
A fellow cried: 'Look at your feet!'
I looked at them and sadly said:
'I 've left them both asleep in bed!'

6

I eat my peas with honey,
　　I 've done it all my life:
It makes the peas taste funny,
　　But it keeps them on the knife.'

7

　　Once upon a time,
　　When the pigs were swine
And the monkeys chewed tobacco:
　　Little pigs took snuff
　　To make them puff,
And little boys said: 'What 's the matt-o?'

8

Oh my mother!　What a fool I be!
Two dead men were chasing me:
One was blind and the other couldn't see. . .
Oh my mother!　What a fool I be!

EPILOGUE

'So she went into the garden to cut a cabbage-leaf to make
an apple-pie; and at the same time a great she-bear, coming
up the street, pops its head into the shop: 'What! no soap?'
So he died, and she very imprudently married the Barber.
And there were present the Picninnies, and the Joblillies,
and the Garyalies, and the grand Panjandrum himself, with
the little round button at top.   And they all fell to playing
the game of catch-as-catch-can, till the gunpowder ran out
at the heels of their boots.'

Samuel Foote (1755).

INDEX OF FIRST LINES OF VERSE